INCLUDING FOLLOW ON ACTIVITIES

EDITED BY IAN LUMSDEN

Published in 1989 by
Unwin Hyman Limited
15–17 Broadwick Street
London W1V 1FP

British Library Cataloguing in Publication Data
Scriptz. — (Unwin Hyman plays).
1. Drama in English, 1945— Texts
I. Lumsden, Ian
822'.914

ISBN 0—04—448124—1

Typeset by TJB Photosetting Ltd., Grantham, Lincolnshire
Printed in Great Britain by Billings & Sons Ltd., Worcester

Series Editor: Roy Blatchford
Series cover design by Iain Lanyon
Cover illustration by Rowan Barnes-Murphy

CONTENTS

Introduction

With the exception of the video tape recorder breaking down or the teacher breaking a leg, there's nothing more likely to engage the interest of a class than a good play; unless, that is, you have two plays. Here we have six good plays and after the main course there's something to follow on. We even throw in the gravy!

Scriptz is a collection of plays intended for a wide age range within the secondary school. The plays represent work from the stage, television and radio. Although varied in subject matter, they are linked in that they all use humour in one form or other. They are not, however, merely a collection of funny plays intended to fill in that awkward spot of last lesson on a wet Thursday afternoon—although they are all weatherproof! They are both humorous and serious. In most cases the humour is the vehicle used to explore quite difficult issues. I believe the plays will engender a spirit of good humour in the classroom and, first and foremost, this was the main criterion governing their selection.

For each play there is a specially written essay by the playwright. Each essay is aimed directly at the pupils and is lively and stimulating in its own right. Just as it is enormously rewarding to have a writer address a class in the flesh, the essays themselves also shed light on the craft of writing as well as illuminating aspects of the text. The essay and play should be treated as a combined resource.

Jackie's First Day by Phil Lowe starts the anthology with a short stage play which is both witty and relevant to all first year pupils who have just started a new school and were worried by the prospect. Jan Mark's *Feet* is a radio play intended for slightly older pupils. The sensitive use of humour in this potentially explosive cocktail of tantrums on the tennis court and wounded feelings makes this a fine example of this acclaimed writer's work.

My own script, *Mm,* is a light-hearted depiction of various adventures enjoyed by, among others, two best friends, a pair of giants, a diminutive removal man and a twelve year old femme fatale called

Lucy-Ann Brown. *Naughty Girls* by Rony Robinson is a very funny radio drama with St Trinianesque echoes and a message for all of us who have ever tried to impress the HMI. It is great fun to read out in class; as is his related 'How Mavis Met Gary Blood' which continues the saga of the naughty girls.

The final play in the collection, Helen Cresswell's *For Bethlehem Read Little Thraves,* is a delightful television script about the Christmas preparations for an infant school's Nativity play. Its warmth and charm will brighten up any classroom regardless of the season.

Ian Lumsden

PHIL LOWE

Jackie's First Day

CHARACTERS

JACKIE
MR BOLTON
KAY
MR BATES
MRS HATHAWAY
HEADMASTER
1ST BULLY
2ND BULLY
ANNOUNCER'S VOICE

NB The gender of any character can be changed without affecting the play.

(*Jackie enters, speaking to the audience.*)

JACKIE I'm Jackie. This is my first day at Hangham High School. It's ever so big—hope I can find my way around. At the moment I'm looking for the cloakroom, so I can leave my coat. I think I'll have to ask someone.

(*Mr Bolton enters, looking confused.*)

JACKIE Excuse me, sir, can you tell me how to get to the cloakroom?

MR BOLTON (*hesitantly*) Ah. The cloakroom. Just a moment.

(*He gets out a large map and consults it.*) Now, you want to go to the end of this corridor, turn left, and then... no, no, hang on, turn *right*, then second left and—*third* left, sorry,... or is it third *right*? (*impatiently*) Oh, look, you take the map—you can bring it to the staff room later.

JACKIE Who shall I ask for, sir?

MR BOLTON Oh, I'm Mr Bolton; I'm the Geography teacher.

(*Jackie wanders off, studying her map. At the cloakroom she comes across Kay, leaning against a wall smoking a curly pipe and trying to look tough.*)

JACKIE (*nervously*) Erm, is this a first year's cloakroom?

KAY Might be. Are you a first year?

JACKIE (*bravely*) Erm, yes I am actually.

KAY (*taking the pipe out of her mouth and smiling with relief*) Oh good, so am I. I'm pretending to be a fourth year so no one's horrible to me.

JACKIE Cor, you had me fooled. We've got our timetabling period now, are you coming?

KAY (*dismayed*) No, I can't. I've got to go to all the fourth year lessons so no one'll guess I'm a first year.

JACKIE But you'll never learn anything if you do that.

KAY I hadn't thought of that. Oh well, I expect I'll work something out.

(*Jackie is in her timetabling class. Mr Bates arrives to take it. For these classroom scenes, Jackie can sit among the audience and the teacher in question can then address everyone*)

MR BATES Good morning good morning. Now, you're 1DCR, is that right? No, no, don't tell me, 1SAC. Great. Now, as you've noticed, you're classed by initials, the initials of your tutor,

eg SAC or DCR, OK? I'm HJB—Mr Bates, sorry. I'm not your tutor, I'm here to timetable you. Right, so if you've got your pens ready, we'll begin:
(*He delivers the following as fast as possible.*) Monday period one is timetabling. Except for every Monday that isn't today, you will have either Biology, Tautology or Chronology, depending on whether your first period on Tuesdays is Geography, Lexicography or Maths. Geography people will do Biology, unless they have Histrionics on a Tuesday, in which case they will still do Biology, but their homework night will be swapped with their Ballistics homework. Those who do Maths on a Tuesday will have half a period of Biology, plus half a period of aerobics unless there is an 'R' in the month, when they do that the other way round. All with me? OK, onto Monday period two...(*A Bell rings.*) Oh dear, we've run right out of time, it's break now. Never mind, I expect you'll pick it up as you go along. (*He exits.*)

JACKIE (*to audience*) It's all a bit confusing. I don't even know how long break lasts. I'll have to be brave and ask someone.
(*Mrs Hathaway enters, looking rather scatty.*) Excuse me, Miss, can you tell me how much longer break goes on for?

MRS HATHAWAY Yes of course. Just a moment.
(*She gets out a large cardboard clock face with moveable hands, and begins to move them around.*) Well, let me see... Break started at 11.05, and finishes at 11.20, and it's now (*consults watch*) 11.12, so if the big hand is here and the little hand is here, and the big hand moves from... Oh, I don't know—here, you see if you can work it out. (*She*

gives Jackie the clock) You can bring that to me later on.

JACKIE Who shall I ask for, Miss?

MRS HATHAWAY Oh, I'm Mrs Hathaway; I'm the Maths teacher.

(*Jackie has found her way to the hall. She sits among the audience.*)

JACKIE (*to audience*) Well, at least I know what *this* period is; it's when the headteacher gives us a talk to welcome us here.

(*The Head arrives, obviously preoccupied, and stands facing away from the audience.*)

HEAD Good morning, I'd like to welc – (*realises he is facing the wrong way and turns round*) Good morning, I'd like to welcome you all to (*forgetting the name*) er..., to Hangham High School. I'm the headmaster, Mr (*checking the label on the inside of his jacket*) Marks and Spencer (*realising*)—Mr Manners, and I'd like to say how pleased we are to welcome you all from..., er, to, er welcome you all, erm, here. Right, now I know it must all seem a bit strange to you at the moment, but believe me, by the time you've been here as long as I have you'll be bound to know where you are. We are now in ...the, er (*suddenly remembering*) the Main Hall, that's right, and the canteen is next to... er... (*sudden inspiration*) If you want to get in or out of the Hall by the way, you should use the doors, that's very important. Now, I'm sure the whole place looks rather large to you—I expect you think it takes hours to get from one end to the other. Well you won't think that for long—not once we build the underground railway to the Chemistry labs. In the meantime, the number 63 bus is quite handy for the woodwork department, or collect your walking boots from my secretary. Anyway, run along to lunch now, and I'll see you soon.

(He exits, going the wrong way and having to come back again.)

JACKIE Perhaps I ought to use my lunch break to wander round and get the feel of the place. (*wandering*) I don't know where I am at the moment—there's no one about and it seems miles from anywhere...

(Two Bullies enter behind Jackie.)

1ST BULLY 'Ere, you a first year?

JACKIE Yes. I expect you're pretending to be a stupid fourth year, aren't you?

1ST BULLY Not quite, shorty. We really *are* fourth years...

JACKIE Oh...

1ST BULLY And we don't like you...

2ND BULLY No...

1ST BULLY We don't like *any* little first years, and we're going to get you...

JACKIE (*quickly*) No, I tell you what, if you let me go I'll give you both a present.

1ST BULLY What kind of present?

JACKIE It's in my bag. I'll just get it.

(She reaches in her bag and pulls out a large cloak.)

1ST BULLY Wassat, a curtain? That's a funny present.

(Jackie, back to the audience, is putting the cloak on.)

'Ere, if you're taking the mickey...

2ND BULLY Yeah...

(Jackie, wearing the cloak, whirls round, transformed.)

BULLIES (*to audience*) OH NO! IT'S SUPER FIRST YEAR!!!

(To the accompaniment of suitable music (either provided by the cast or on tape) Super First Year makes mincemeat of the bullies in comical slow motion.)

ANNOUNCER'S VOICE 'Once again the school is safe, and its pupils can walk the corridors without fear... thanks to SUPER FIRST YEAR!!!'

(*The cast raise Jackie up in the air and fly her offstage.*)

PHIL LOWE

An Apology

When I sat down with the intention of writing about *Jackie's First Day,* I felt that I really should be apologising for it. Looking at it now, it seems such a short little play, not really about very much at all, that I find myself wondering whether anyone will actually bother to read it. But this of course is how all writers spend their days—none of us can ever believe that people actually want to sit down and read the words we sweated and struggled over months, sometimes years, earlier. Alright then, I won't apologise. So what if it's short? So was Napoleon, and he did alright for himself. No, what I would rather do, before I run out of introduction, is to explain how a short little play about nothing very much came to be written in the first place.

At the time I wrote *Jackie's First Day* I was working for the Touchstone Theatre-in-Education Company, based in Essex. I imagine many of you have had theatre companies visiting your school at one time or another. They are usually one of two sorts: the ones who come in and perform a play (which is OK because you can sit at the back and flick things at the person in front), or the ones who make you sit in a circle and talk about the play they've come in to do (which makes it difficult to flick things at anyone, unless you flick them at one of the actors—although because actors aren't as responsible as teachers, they'll probably come up to you after the show and clobber you). Touchstone was one of the second sort of companies. Our plays tended to deal with important issues such as drug abuse, or drink driving, the sort of subjects that really need a workshop or discussion on them, as well as a play. So what would happen would be that I would be asked to write a play around a given topic, and then we would visit a school, run a workshop on the topic with a group of pupils, and then perform the play.

Jackie's First Day was produced like that. A secondary school in Harlow asked us to provide a workshop for a group of children from local junior schools, who were going to be moving up to the secondary school next term. We decided that the session would finish with a short play, which I was to write. During the session we were going to be dwelling on some of the things that frighten people about moving up to a big school, and we wanted to end on a positive note. I decided to write a play which made fun of some of the worries that juniors in that situation have—not being able to find your way around, too many teachers, timetables, being bullied—so that when the audience thought about any of their fears, they might also remember laughing at them in the play, and feel a bit better about it.

A lot of people are surprised that most of the plays I have written have been effectively written to order; certainly when you're at school, sitting in an English lesson having just been told to write a 500 word essay beginning 'I woke up one morning to find my feet had turned into a liver and bacon casserole…', you probably find yourself thinking how brilliant it must be to be a professional writer, being able to write whatever you like and getting paid for it. This, I am afraid, is not usually the case. Most of us live by being able to turn our hand to whatever needs doing. But that isn't necessarily a bad thing. I remember the first story I ever had published; I was still at school, and my English teacher asked me if I would be interested in sending something to a publishers who were looking for short stories. The only thing was it would have to be a love story aimed at fourteen year-old girls. Now, as you may well imagine, asking a streetcool teenage hipster like me to write a soppy love story for girls did not get a very positive response, until I thought about it, and decided that what I would do would be to write a bitter and twisted love story that would really give them something to think about. And of course, in the end it stood out from all the soppy love stories and they published it. Since then, if I'm asked to write about a given subject, I never write what I think they want me to write; I take the topic and I write about it how I want to; in short, I make it *mine*. That's what writers do; there are never enough new subjects to write about, so they take an old one, and make it their own.

So, now you have read the play, you might like to think about what sort of play *you* might have written in the same situation; and think, also, about how not every play that is written is a huge play about enormous earth-shattering subjects—sometimes a short little play about nothing very much has a point—it all depends what you're writing it for.

JAN MARK

Feet

CHARACTERS

JANE
DIANE *Fourth Year girls at a comprehensive. About fifteen.*
RUTH

CARSON
COLLIER *Sixth Formers at the same school. Eighteen.*
MILLS
McGARRITY

MR EVANS *Games teachers.*
MISS TRUMAN

DAWN *Jane's cousin. About seventeen.*

They are all from the South East except for Evans (Welsh), McGarrity (Scottish) and Dawn, who just comes from somewhere else. They all have strong to middling local accents although Carson is acquiring polish and Collier is downright smooth.

(*Interior acoustic. A crowded bus. Diesel engine and voices in background. Hold.*)

DAWN What's *his* name?

JANE Who?

DAWN The one who just changed seats.

JANE Oh—Gorman or Goblin or something. I don't know *him*.

DAWN What about that one who got on when we did?

JANE Which one?

DAWN The one who nearly missed it. He had to run.

JANE That's Alan Carson.

DAWN He looks nice.

JANE Don't keep *staring*. He's all right.

DAWN Isn't he the one who used to babysit with you? (*Bus stops.*)

JANE Ssssh! That was ages ago. Anyway, it wasn't me he was sitting with, it was Kevin. Mum didn't think it was right leaving me to look after him in the evenings.

DAWN Hey—who's *that*?

JANE (*elaborately unconcerned*) Which one? (*Bus starts.*)

DAWN The one who went upstairs—with the dark hair.

JANE That's Collier. Michael Collier.

DAWN He's something else, isn't he?

JANE Mmmm...

DAWN Is he still at school? He looks rather older.

JANE He leaves this term. He's going to University in the Autumn. (*Without enthusiasm*) So's Carson. Most of them are. But Michael—Collier—he—

DAWN You got something going for him?

JANE No!

DAWN You have.

JANE Shut up. He doesn't know I exist.

DAWN His legs go all the way up, don't they? (*Bus stops.*)

JANE Oh, you should see him in shorts. He's our tennis star. I don't know why he doesn't go professional. He just walks all over everybody. We've got the school tournament next week—he's bound to win it. I put my name down to be umpire. I might get to umpire one of his matches.

DIANE Come on, Turner. Shove up. You can get another one on there. (*Bus starts.*)

JANE Oh, hullo Di. Can you squeeze up a bit, Dawn? Di, this is my cousin Dawn. Mind your feet.

DIANE Sorry—thanks. Did you say you were umpiring?

JANE If I can get round Mr Evans.

DAWN Who's he?

DIANE Our games master.

JANE Or Miss Truman. She's our lady games master. No good getting round *her,* though. She thinks I'm an imbecile. I've heard her.

DAWN Look, don't I have to get out along here?

JANE Oh...yeah. The bus stops by Woolies. If you go on up past Boots you come to Debenhams...

(*Fade out.*)

(*Fade in interior acoustic. Gymnasium noises.*)

EVANS Jane! Jane Turner!

JANE (*approaching*) Sir?

EVANS I see you've put your name down to umpire at the tournament next week.

JANE Yes. It's all right, isn't it? You don't mind, do you, sir?

EVANS Mind? No, of course not. But I didn't know you were interested.

JANE I've done it for junior matches, sir. I can *play.*

EVANS Why didn't you enter for the tournament, then?

JANE Oh, I don't play that well. I'm not all that bad, actually, sir, but I go to pieces if anyone's watching.

EVANS You won't go to pieces if anyone watches you umpiring?

JANE Oh no, sir. That's different.

EVANS You'll still have to concentrate.

JANE I do concentrate.

EVANS On the court *and* on the score card. Miss Truman thinks—

JANE Oh...

EVANS Perhaps we could put you on Centre Court as it's your first time—in the big time, that is.

JANE Centre Court! Oh, *sir.*

EVANS It won't matter so much if you make mistakes...

(*Fade out.*) (*Fade in interior acoustic. The bus. Hold.*)

DAWN What d'you think of this, then?

JANE Brilliant.

DAWN It'd look all right with these sandals, I thought.
(*Rustling of paper.*)

DAWN Well, that's the lot. Did you have a good day?

JANE Sort of. I saw old Evans about the umpiring. He said I could do it.

DAWN Brilliant.

JANE Yes...but he's putting me on Centre Court.

DAWN I thought you said you hadn't done big matches before. He must think a lot of you.

JANE You haven't seen Centre Court. It's not like Centre Court at Wimbledon. It's the one *no* one wants to play on. All the others are grass. Centre Court's asphalt. It's got dents in it, like Ryvita. When there's a governors' meeting they use it as a car park.

DAWN Sounds like the surface of the moon.

JANE Yes. The side the sun doesn't shine on. It's got algae growing round the edges—like mould on cheese. It's bright green. It's where they put all the little juniors who can't see over the net.

DAWN What'sisname won't be playing on it, then? Collier.

JANE Fat chance. It'll be all Ladies Doubles—that's Fifth and Sixth year girls. Knock knees and big backsides.

DAWN Ladies Trebles.
(*Bus stops.*)

JANE All the junior boys come along to look at the legs and things—and the men teachers. They pretend they're just passing, only there's nowhere to go. Old Truman caught them once. She didn't half lead off.

DAWN I'm glad I went to an all-girls school. There was nothing like that.
(*Bus starts.*)

JANE (*sly*) No Colliers, either.

DAWN You don't have to go to school to find Colliers. Two a penny, Colliers are. He gave me a *look* just now, when he got off.

JANE Really? I didn't notice him.

DAWN He was upstairs. Having a fag, I suppose.

JANE Oh no! He doesn't smoke. He's terrifically fit. He's got this terrific service, goes up about ten *yards*...

DAWN (*darkly*) Probably on steroids...

(*Fade out.*)

(*Exterior acoustic. Passing traffic. Hold.*)

CARSON Morning.

JANE Hullo, Carson.

CARSON Ho! Me Carson, you Jane. (*Ululates.*)

JANE Be quiet. People are looking.

CARSON So don't be so soft. What's wrong with Alan?

JANE Well, *you* know...at school...

CARSON It makes me feel like I was in the army. Private 069280119 Carson A J C, reporting dead, sir!

JANE Sorry. Alan.

CARSON That's more like it. Where's your friend this morning?

JANE Friend?

CARSON That blonde on the bus yesterday. The one with the funny ideas about colour co-ordinates and cabriole legs.

JANE You are rotten. That's my cousin Dawn. She's got terrific style. What's wrong with her legs?

CARSON Nothing. They'd look very good on a Chippendale chair.

JANE Well, she's only here till Thursday next.

CARSON She coming to the tournament?

JANE Shouldn't think so.

CARSON You mean, she'd pass up the chance to see me on court?

JANE She's got a steady fellow. Anyway, Collier'll win, won't he?

CARSON Oh, Jane, you're so tactful.

JANE (*hurriedly*) Well, you're second favourite but, I mean, everyone *expects* Collier to win, don't they?

CARSON So does Collier. I don't know why he bothers to

play, really. They might just as well give him the trophy and have done with it.

JANE (*trying to make amends*) And Mills and McGarrity will be in the semi-final probably, won't they? I mean, it'll be a good competition.

CARSON It'll be the Saint Valentine's Day Massacre all over again. Added to which, the standard of umpiring's going down, I hear. In-ex-or-ab-ly.

JANE Whaddya mean?

CARSON Someone told me you're an umpire this year.

JANE You *are* rotten.

CARSON To the core. Which court are you on?

JANE (*mumbling*) Centre Court.

CARSON Where?

JANE Centre Court! Mr Evans said it won't matter so much if I make mistakes.

CARSON No one'll notice if you make mistakes. They'll be too busy trying to estimate the angle of ricochet every time the ball hits a pot hole...

(*Bus approaches. Fade out.*)

(*Interior acoustic. Outside the changing rooms. Footsteps. Voices. Locker doors slamming.*)

RUTH ...and Collier's got one of those new raquets.

CARSON What, the kind with holes in?

RUTH No, carbon fibre, or something. Or is it cobalt?

CARSON Enriched plutonium?

DIANE Oh, shut up, Carson.

CARSON (*plaintive*) I've only got an old wooden one. My grandfather made it himself with a knapped flint. Hey, McGarrity, coming out for a knock-up?

MCGARRITY Court Five? See you out there.

DIANE That Carson. Thinks he's so funny.

JANE Oh, he's all right.

DIANE I forgot you knew him at home. He used to babysit when you were little, didn't he?

JANE Not with *me*. With my brother. What court are you on, Ruth?

RUTH Three. Mills versus Atkinson, for starters.

JANE That'll be a walkover.

DIANE Who've you got?

JANE I dunno. It's Ladies Doubles. Let's have a look.

RUTH They always put Ladies Doubles on Centre Court. Shows what they think of us, doesn't it?

DIANE Why don't they put the Men's Doubles out there, for once?

JANE The boys'd kick up.

RUTH Why don't we kick up?

JANE We aren't playing.

RUTH Not just us—all the girls. It's the same with hockey. We always get the pitch with the one-in-five slope. Half the goals are due to gravity.

DIANE Hadn't you two better get on out there?

JANE You coming to watch?

DIANE Not on *your* court...

(*Fade out.*)

(*Exterior acoustic. Slight echo.*)

JANE It's like being at the bottom of the Grand Canyon, down here.

RUTH If the Science block wasn't there it wouldn't be so bad. The light's terrible.

JANE At least we don't get people griping about the sun in their eyes.

TRUMAN Now then, you two, which courts are you supposed to be on?

RUTH Court Three, Miss Truman.

TRUMAN Well, you'd better get along there, hadn't you? You're on this court, aren't you, Jane?

JANE Yes, Miss.

TRUMAN Where are your ball boys?

JANE I don't know. Nobody told me—

TRUMAN It's on the *list*. Umpires are supposed to make the courts ready for the first game. Did you bring the balls out?

JANE Oh, yes, Miss.

TRUMAN Score cards?

JANE Yes.

TRUMAN You've got a pencil?

JANE *Yes*.

TRUMAN (*evidently disappointed*) All right, then. Now, for heaven's sake pay attention to what you're doing. You're not very suitably dressed, are you? Haven't you got a cardigan?

JANE No.

TRUMAN And you've got gooseflesh on your legs already. Why on earth didn't you wear a track suit—or tights. Those sandals would be all right for a disco—

JANE I'm fine.

TRUMAN And nail varnish! (*Going*) It's not as if anyone's going to be looking at *your* feet...

(*Fade out.*)

(*Fade in, the same.*)

JANE (*calling*) Fifteen – thirty!

(*Service and return.*)

Thirty all!

(*Service and return.*)

Thirty – forty!

(*Service and rally.*)

Game, set and match!

(*Thin applause.*)

DIANE Who won that, then?

JANE Lisa Young and Helen Gallacher. Well, they didn't win, the other two lost. How're the men doing?

DIANE Oh, Mills is beating Symonds, McGarrity's beaten Daintry, Carson's going to beat Baldwin and Collier's flattened Innis. I dunno how the girls are doing. I haven't been watching.

JANE I hope I finish here in time for the final. I've got two more Ladies Doubles yet.

DIANE Here comes your next lot.

JANE Oh...*them*.

(*Fade out.*)

(*Fade in the same.*)

(*Service and return.*)

Deuce!

(*Service.*)

Advantage server!

(*Service and rally.*)

Game, set and match!

(*Thin applause.*)

RUTH You got time for a drink, then, Jane? You look frozen.

JANE I am frozen. It's like sitting on top of Mount Everest, up here.

RUTH Shall I get them to send something out? Tea or coffee?

JANE Just boiling water would do. No—it's all right. I'll come in for a bit.

RUTH What about your next match?

JANE They're late—they can wait. If I get any colder I shan't be able to hold the pencil. The marks are getting all wobbly with shivering.

RUTH (*going*) See you over there, then. Hey, you got a visitor.

CARSON Ho. You Jane, me crippled. Ouch! You don't mind if I sit on your ladder for a bit? I'm in great pain.

JANE Is that why you're limping?

CARSON No, I'm limping because it looks distinguished. You ever tried walking without touching the ground?

JANE You look like Richard the Third. What have you done?

CARSON My ankle. I think I shall die here. Nip round ours tonight, will you, and tell Mum I made a good end.

(*Death rattle.*)

JANE Did you lose your match?

CARSON No, I won it, but it was a Pyrrhic victory.

JANE What's a Pyrrhic victory?

CARSON One you can do without. Named after King Pyrrhus of Epirus who remarked, after beating the Romans in a battle, 'One more win like this and we've had it,' on account of the Romans badly chewing up his army.

JANE (*lost*) Oh. Did he get another win?

CARSON Yes, but then he got done over at the Battle of Beneventum by Curius Dentatus the famous Roman general with funny teeth.

JANE Did he really have funny teeth?

CARSON Eh?

JANE I mean, is that what he was famous for?

CARSON You don't do Latin, do you?

JANE I took the Science option.

CARSON Never mind. I just knocked spots off Pete Baldwin in the quarter-final, and I'm just running up the net to thank him for a jolly-good-game-old-boy when I turn my ankle and fall flat on my back. It's a good thing I didn't get as far as the net. I might have jumped over it and *then* fallen flat on my back.

JANE That's the kind of thing that happens to me.

CARSON I should have met Mick Collier in the semi-final. Now he'll have a walkover—which should suit him. He doesn't care where he puts his feet.

JANE Nobody looks at feet. Who will he meet in the final?

CARSON This is not the response I was looking for.

JANE What?

CARSON You are supposed to say 'Oh, Alan, what a frightful shame. You would surely have beaten Collier.'

JANE But I only—oh, sorry. It isn't half swelling, isn't it? Who will Collier play in the final?

CARSON (*fed up*) Mills or McGarrity. Mills is currently beating McGarrity and then Collier will beat Mills—to pulp—and no one will be in the least surprised. I don't know why we bother. (*Going*) It was a foregone conclusion...

JANE (*contrite*) I should get that bandaged up.

CARSON (*distant*) I think I'll get it amputated...

(*Thunder.*)

RUTH Jane. Hey, Jane. Oi!

JANE Wha-a-a-at?

RUTH You're not sticking up there, are you? You'll get struck.

JANE Struck?

(*Thunder.*)

RUTH By lightning, Dimbo. Look at the sky.

JANE Oh. Hey, Collier's in the final.

RUTH Of course he is. Tell me something I don't know. Oh, come on down.

JANE I've still got another match to go. They'll be out any minute.

RUTH Look, it's starting to rain. Come *on*.

(*Thunder. Sudden downpour. Fade out.*)

(*Fade in interior acoustic. Tennis rhubarb in background. Hold.*)

DIANE I think it's stopping.

MCGARRITY It'll be too wet to go on the grass again.

MILLS We'll have to finish up on Centre Court.

(*Derisive laughter.*)

RUTH How's it going, Mills?

MILLS Four – six, six – love, four – one at the moment. If it'd held off for another ten minutes I'd have cleaned up.

MCGARRITY Oh yeah?

MILLS Sorry, McGarrity. Didn't see you there.

DIANE Well, one of you's going to face Collier in the final.

MILLS Ah, a worthy opponent.

MCGARRITY Meaning what?

EVANS Cool it, you two. Keep the aggro for the match. Miss Truman and I will go out and see what the grass is like. (*Going*) Does anyone know how Carson is?

MILLS (*going*) He was strapping his foot up just now. It looks pretty nasty.

RUTH D'you want to borrow my sweater, Jane? You're all over blue blotches. Jane. Jane!

JANE Collier keeps looking at me.

RUTH (*frankly*) I don't think so.

JANE He does. Every time I look at him he sort of catches my eye and then looks away.

DIANE Trick of the light.

JANE He's coming over.

DIANE You're hallucinating. (*Going*) Hey, look at old Truman skidding about with Evans...

RUTH (*going*) Torvill and Dean.

COLLIER Hullo-o-o-o.

JANE (*croaks*)

COLLIER Jane Turner, isn't it?

JANE (*breathless*) Yes.

COLLIER Thought so. I see you on the bus, don't I?

JANE Yes.

COLLIER You're an umpire today, aren't you?

JANE Yes.

COLLIER Do you play?

JANE Yes. A bit.

COLLIER (*coaxing*) Which bit?

JANE Oh...I mean...I play sometimes. I'm not too bad —not in *your* class...

COLLIER No. We have a court at home.

JANE Yes.

COLLIER You ought to come over and play, sometime.

JANE (*incredulous*) Oh! Oh yes! Yes *please*. Yes. I'd like that.

COLLIER You can bring your cousin and make up a foursome. That was your cousin who was sitting on the bus with you, wasn't it?

JANE Oh yes. Dawn. She's only—

COLLIER Come on Friday, then. About seven-thirty?

DAWN Oh, yes. Actually Dawn's only—

EVANS (*approaching*) Well, the grass is kaput. It's like the Empire Pool Wembley out there.

COLLIER Have we had it, then?

TRUMAN The grass has had it.

MILLS What about Centre Court?

EVANS Well...how do *you* feel about Centre Court?

COLLIER I'd rather play on Centre Court than not play at all.

TRUMAN Mills?

MILLS Same here.

EVANS Right. Come on Collier. Come on Mills.

MCGARRITY (*nasty*) Mills hasn't beaten me yet, sir.

EVANS Oh...

TRUMAN Well, hurry up and finish him off, Mills.

MCGARRITY (*growls*)

EVANS Where's the umpire?

JANE It's me, sir.

EVANS Ah.

JANE You *told* me to go on Centre Court, sir.

EVANS Hmmm. Can you manage?

JANE I haven't made any mistakes yet, sir.

EVANS Well...

TRUMAN But it's the *final*.

MCGARRITY (*low and threatening*) Not yet, it isn't.

JANE Oh, sir, *please*. Please, sir.

TRUMAN Look, David, this is ridiculous.

EVANS We'll see what she makes of Mills and McGarrity.

TRUMAN (*going*) If you saw as much of that girl as I do...

EVANS I haven't seen anything to complain of yet. (*Going*) Get a move on, you lot.

RUTH I bet he lets you do it just to spite her...

(*Fade out.*)

(*Exterior acoustic. Centre court. The echo.*)

JANE (*confident*) McGarrity to serve!

(*Service.*)

JANE Fault!

(*Service.*)

Love – fifteen!

(*Service and return.*)

Love – thirty!

(*Service.*)

Out!

(*Service and rally.*)

Love – forty!

(*Service and volley.*)

(*Applause. Hold.*)

Game, set and match to Neil Mills.

CARSON That was another foregone conclusion.

JANE Oh! It's you. I'm doing all right, aren't I?

CARSON But of course. *I'm* sinking fast.

JANE How is your foot?

CARSON Basically it's still attached to the end of my leg, but the prognosis is doubtful. I think it's traumatised. When I wake up in the morning it will be hanging by a thread.

JANE (*absently*) You should get it seen to. Oh, sir, I'm managing, aren't I?

EVANS You did very well, Jane. Think you can keep it up?

JANE Oh, yes sir. *Please*.

EVANS I don't see why not. Ah, Alan, how's the damage?

CARSON (*straight*) I think I've cracked a bone, sir.

EVANS Shouldn't you be resting it? I thought I told you to go home.

CARSON I want to watch the final. This may be my last chance ever to see Collier in action. Oh, please, sir, don't deny me that.

EVANS You're a sarcastic so-and-so, aren't you?

CARSON Just don't belong to the fan club, sir.

EVANS Here they come, Jane. On your toes.

MILLS Oh, *you're* umpiring again, are you?

JANE (*bold*) Any complaints?

MILLS Just so long as you're impartial.

JANE I was impartial when you were playing McGarrity.

MILLS (*going*) So?

CARSON Good luck, Sunshine.

COLLIER Hullo, umpire.

JANE Hullo Coll—er—Michael.

COLLIER Don't be too hard on me, Jane.

JANE I've got to be impartial.

COLLIER I won't hold that against you. Don't forget Friday.

JANE (*overloud*) I won't forget Friday.

RUTH *ET AL* (*Murmurs of surprise*.)

COLLIER (*distant*) And don't forget your cousin.

JANE Oh, she won't be able to make it.

COLLIER What!

JANE I was trying to tell you—she's going home tomorrow.

COLLIER Some other time, then.

JANE No, no. *I* can come on Friday.

COLLIER (*ungracious and loud*) No, it doesn't matter.

RUTH *What's* all this about Friday?

DIANE Someone got the wrong end of the stick. I said you were hallucinating.

(*Sounds of knock-up on court. Hold.*)

JANE Oh, shut up.

DIANE You didn't think he was after *you*, did you?

RUTH (*Giggles.*)

JANE Ow!

RUTH What happened? Your heart broken?

JANE (*near to tears*) My pencil.

DIANE You're blushing, look. Right down to your ankles.

JANE Shut up. *Shut up.*

CARSON (*muttering*) You're meant to be starting them off. Collier won the toss—naturally.

DIANE Your glasses have steamed up.

JANE (*quavering*) Play, please. Collier to serve!

CARSON Let him get on with it. If he won't play with you on Friday he can play with himself.

(*Service and return.*)

JANE Oh, Alan...

CARSON Watch the court, for God's sake. That was a point to Collier.

JANE Fifteen – love!

(*Service and return.*)

Thirty – love!

(*Service and applause.*)

Forty – love!

(*Service and return.*)

Forty – fifteen!

(*Service and rally.*)

Game to Collier!

CARSON Told you it would be a walkover...

(*Fade out.*)

(*Fade in.*)

JANE Advantage Collier!

(*Service and return.*)

Deuce!

(*Service and rally.*)

Advantage Mills!
(*Service.*)
Game to Mills! Collier leads five games to two in the first set!

CARSON He's not having it all his own way.

JANE Near enough.

CARSON Jane, pull yourself together. You won't be able to see what you're doing.

JANE I can't see what I'm doing anyway. I broke the pencil and the lines are all coming out double. haven't got one, have you?

CARSON Sorry—no.

JANE He won't look at me.

CARSON Why should he? They're only changing ends.

JANE But he keeps *not* looking at me. He's definitely *not* looking at me.

CARSON I'm definitely *not* looking at him. Think he cares?
(*Service.*)
Fifteen – love. Watch the *court.*

JANE Fifteen – love!
(*Fade out.*)
(*Fade in service and volley.*)

JANE Thirty – all!

COLLIER (*distant*) *What*?

JANE Sorry...thirty – forty...no! Forty – thirty!
(*Service.*)
Deuce! (*Whispers*) Was it?

CARSON (*whispers*) Yes.
(*Service.*)

JANE Advantage Mills!

COLLIER *Whaddya* say?

JANE (*panic*) Deuce—no—advantage Collier!
(*Service, return and volley. Fade out.*)
(*Fade in.*)
Advantage Mills!

COLLIER It's forty – thirty to *me*, damn you.

JANE Oh! Oh, yes...sorry.
(*Service.*)
Game to—deuce—no...

COLLIER (*close and muttering*) This is all I need—a cross-eyed umpire. There're eight hundred people in this school. Can't we find *one* with 20 – 20 vision?

JANE I'm *sorry.*

(*Service and rally. Hold.*)

CARSON I told you, didn't I? This guy doesn't care *where* he puts his feet.

JANE What? Game to Collier! What?

CARSON He's treading all over *your* corns for a start, isn't he?

(*Service.*)

JANE Fifteen – love!

(*Service and volley.*)

Out!

COLLIER It was not.

JANE It was. I...I...

COLLIER It was on the line.

CARSON (*low*) It was out.

JANE Out!

COLLIER (*calling to spectators*) Was that out or was that out?

(*Embarrassed mumbling.*)

JANE I thought...

COLLIER It was in.

JANE Thirty – love!

COLLIER For God's sake clean your glasses.

(*Service and rally. Hold.*)

CARSON And that was a foot fault.

JANE Was it?

CARSON Too late now. Forty – love.

JANE Forty – love!

(*Service and return.*)

CARSON Toes over the base line. Like I said, he doesn't care where he puts his feet.

JANE Game to Collier! Collier leads four games to one in the second set and one set to love! I didn't realise you meant real feet.

CARSON I didn't. But you watch them next time he serves.

JANE It's Mills to serve next. Are you sure?

CARSON Can't take my eyes off them. They're so *shapely.*

(*Service and return.*)

JANE Fifteen – love!

CARSON Of course, Mills might win this game anyway...

(*Fade out.*)

(*Fade in.*)

JANE Game to Mills! Collier leads four games to two in the second set and one set to love.

CARSON Right. Now, watch him.

JANE It's that fantastic service. He doesn't look at his feet.

CARSON Exactly. Nobody looks at feet.

JANE He doesn't do it on purpose.

CARSON He shouldn't do it at all.

JANE But what shall *I* do?

CARSON You're the umpire. Call him out.

(*Service and return.*)

JANE Fifteen – love!

CARSON Jane, his *feet*.

JANE I'll give him one last chance.

CARSON (*firm*) He's had his chance.

(*Service and applause. Hold.*)

CARSON *Jane*.

JANE Foot fault!

(*Surprised mumbling.*)

Second service!

(*Service.*)

Out! Fifteen all!

(*Service.*)

Foot fault! Second service!

(*Service and return.*)

Fifteen – thirty!

CARSON (*bland*) His second service isn't very good, really, is it?

(*Service.*)

JANE Out!

(*Service and return.*)

Fifteen – forty!

(*Service.*)

Foot fault!

(*Service and return.*)

Game to Mills! Collier leads four games to three in the second set and one set to love.

(*Fade out.*)

(*Fade in.*)

Love – forty!

(*Service and return.*)

Game to Mills! Mills wins the second set by six games to four!

(*Applause.*)

COLLIER (*close*) What the hell are you playing at, Turner?

JANE What?

COLLIER You know perfectly well what I mean.

JANE I never call foot fault if it isn't one.

COLLIER You vindictive little cow.

MILLS (*distant*) Oi! Mick! We don't change ends yet.

COLLIER (*going*) You shut up...

JANE Oh, Alan, d'you think I —

CARSON You keep it up, girl. Great stuff. Haven't enjoyed a game so much in years.

(*Fade out.*)

(*Fade in. Laughter.*)

CARSON Oh my, he's really going to pieces, isn't he?

JANE Second service!

(*More laughter.*)

CARSON Oh dear, now he's fallen over.

JANE (*appalled*) What happened?

CARSON I think he must have trodden on his own foot. That algae leaves an awful stain, doesn't it?

(*Service.*)

JANE Love – thirty! I think Mills is going to win this.

CARSON I think you are.

JANE Oh...don't.

CARSON Two Pyrrhic victories in one afternoon? That must be a record.

JANE It must be. It's got a hole in it.

(*Service.*)

(*anguished howl*) Foot fault!

(*Fade out.*)

JAN MARK

Personal Essay

I wasn't quite born in the Dark Ages, but we never had a television set all the time I was at school. Consequently, I grew up accustomed to *hearing* great sporting events, on the radio, rather than seeing them; The Grand National, The Test Match, The Boat Race, Wimbledon. The commentary was important, of course, but the noises off—applause, hoofbeats, leather on willow—were essential; a sound track to a film that didn't exist. Radio does give you pictures too, but they are in your head. I think this may be why I can now so easily visualise a story as I write it, and rather a lot of my stories take place while something else is going on in the background; a rehearsal, a choir practice, a bus journey, a carol singing expedition. In *Feet* it is a game of tennis.

I often think back to my schooldays when I write, to relive not the moments of happy triumph, excitement, success, but the hurtful, embarrassing, humiliating things that I would like to forget and cannot. (I am not alone in this.) Some people seem to be able to shrug off hard times and failures with a joke. I've never been able to do that, but I do find I can sometimes lay a bad memory to rest by using it in a story. This doesn't involve writing up exactly what happened—after all, my business is fiction, not autobiography—but a remembered event is often the basis for the fiction I write, and this is what happened with *Feet*.

Before I turned it into a radio play it was a short story which I wrote in 1979, but it was based on an incident which took place in 1959. I was umpiring a tennis tournament between our school and the Boys' Grammar, from the other end of town. One of the lads had his girlfriend along to watch, and he clearly felt that my scoring did not reflect his prowess adequately. He began to argue with me, dispute line calls, challenge the score, and I had no idea how to handle him. *In those days, you did not argue with the umpire*. It was unheard of. By 1979 we were getting used to seeing evil-tempered tennis professionals on television, but even so, it was nothing to the kind of incident that now occurs in Grand Slam matches where inflated sums of prize money are at stake. When it happens to Jane, in *Feet*, she is as taken aback as I was, all those years before.

Now, I am not Jane, and what happened to me is not quite what happens to her—but as I said, I'm not that interested in sticking to the facts. All I need to get going is an idea, and that lout who spoiled my Saturday morning back in 1959 was the idea behind *Feet*. You can see what I mean now about exorcising bad memories. Revenge! Jane gets her revenge on court. I had to wait twenty years for mine, but it was just as satisfying.

Mm

IAN LUMSDEN

CHARACTERS

DAVID
MRS HANNIGAN
MR HANNIGAN — *David's parents*
ALLEN
MRS BERNARD
MR BERNARD — *Allen's parents*
MATTHEW WILDER
LUCY-ANN BROWN — *School friends*
PETE
GIANT — *Removal men*
JOHNNY BROWN — *Lucy-Ann's father*
BARGEE
GEOFFREY — *A large bargee*

1 *The Hannigans' breakfast table*

(As David is rushing his cornflakes, Mrs Hannigan is casting increasingly irritated glances in his direction. Mr Hannigan has his head buried in a newspaper. The radio is playing. Mrs Hannigan switches it off with an angry flourish. No-one takes any notice. All the time she is speaking she is eating a piece of toast.)

MRS H Look, David, there's plenty of time to eat your breakfast. You'll choke. If I know that Bernard woman she won't even be up yet let alone packed and ready to move house. Now just calm down will you, you're getting me all agitated!

DAVID But mum...

MRS H Calm down, David.

DAVID But mum...

MRS H Calm down, David.

DAVID But mum...

MRS H CALM...DOWN...DAVID!

(*She slams her hand down on the table. Milk is spilt on Mr Hannigan's trousers. He rather wearily wipes it up before speaking.*)

MR H You're shouting, dear.

MRS H (*with a false sweetness*) That's nice of you to keep me informed, darling. However, just in case you missed it, I was telling David to calm down, that's all. We don't want him to choke to death, do we.

(*Mr Hannigan smiles and tries once more to hide in his newspaper. She pulls it to one side to stare him in the face.*)

MRS H Sorry to disrupt your reading of the morning newspaper, darling, I realise you like to keep informed but I did feel it important for my son, our son, David, to eat his breakfast without choking. Don't you agree, darling.

MR H Mm.

MRS H 'Mm'? What do you mean, 'Mm'? What exactly does 'Mm' mean?

(*She looks around for support in her argument. David avoids her eyes and eats his breakfast as fast as he can. As Mrs Hannigan continues talking she snatches Mr Hannigan's paper away from him folding it neatly away.*)

MRS H After all, 'Mm' is not a word, not in my copy of the dictionary anyway, but there again perhaps I should be glad of any form of communication at this time in the morning. 'Mm' is uncommonly chatty when I come to think of it

—you're not noted for your conversation, are you, darling?

MR H Do try and calm down, Andrea…

MRS H Calm down! Calm down! How dare you tell me to calm down! Are you saying I'm not calm? Go on, are you, are you? Don't avoid me. At least have the courtesy to look at me while I'm shouting at you!

(She suddenly chokes on a piece of toast. As she splutters and writhes around on the carpet Mr Hannigan goes to help but she pushes him away. We see a close-up of Mr Hannigan's face as he watches his son creep out of the room. He mouths a silent 'Help me'. Mrs Hannigan is recovering and beginning to clench her fist. David is apologetic but clearly unwilling to face his mother's anger. He leaves quickly. His father slowly turns towards Mrs Hannigan.)

2 *The front of David's home*

(It is a detached house in a modern estate. Through the front window David can see his mother hitting his father with the rolled up newspaper. He is not looking where he is going and Matthew Wilder nearly runs into him on his extremely flash racing bike.)

MATTHEW Out of the road, Hannigan, or I'll squash you all over the road! (*David ignores him and breaks into a trot. Wilder cycles alongside him on the pavement.*) You hear me, Hannigan, or were you born deaf as well as daft? I don't like you one bit, Hannigan, I'm gonna burst you one of these days, just you wait, I'm gonna burst you, you hear, Hannigan.

DAVID Why don't you go play wheelies on your bicycle, Wilder.

MATTHEW You won't be so brave when Allen Bernard leaves for Birmingham. You'll be on your own then. You watch, I'll crunch you then, you watch if I don't, I'll crunch you then.

DAVID I'm not a bar of chocolate.

MATTHEW What?

DAVID I crunch bars of chocolate.

MATTHEW What are you on about?

3 *The outside of the Bernards' house*

(*It is a large Victorian semi. Blocking the drive is a removal van which also blocks the pavement.*)

DAVID They're here already.

MATTHEW That's against the law! They're not allowed to block the pavement like that. I'll have to cycle on the road now and my mum's told me I'm not allowed on the road with my new bike, I only got a racer on condition I keep to the pavement.

(*David climbs over the fence. Matthew watches rather forlornly.*)

MATTHEW Will you play with me when Allen leaves? I'll let you have a go on my bike.

DAVID (*from the top of the fence*) Mm.

MATTHEW Yeah, well don't think you're gonna get in the football team when Bernard leaves 'cos you're not!

DAVID Who says?

MATTHEW Mr Dalglish says, that's who.

DAVID Yeah!

MATTHEW Yeah. He told us in Geography, said I was first reserve and I'd got to practise this summer.

DAVID Yeah.

MATTHEW Yeah. Said you play like a powder puff!

DAVID He didn't!

MATTHEW He did!

DAVID Did he?

MATTHEW Yeah!

MATTHEW Did he really?

MATTHEW Yeah! Like a powder puff!

(David disappears over the fence looking downcast. Matthew is pleased with himself and does a wheelie on his bike. He falls off. Springing to his feet he looks to see if anyone has noticed. No one has so he remounts and proceeds as if nothing had happened.)

4 The Bernards' front garden

(A large piano is being manoeuvred through the front door. Pete, a tiny removal man, is struggling backwards supporting most of the weight. He seems about to collapse at any moment. David is hovering at the door waiting to enter.)

PETE Go easy, Joe, go easy!

(The piano emerges through the door. At the other end is Joe, the complete opposite of Pete. He is a giant. He holds the piano effortlessly. As he speaks to David he uses one hand to emphasise his points. Each time he does this it increases the load on his partner who is increasingly near collapse.)

GIANT Good morning, lovely morning.

DAVID Yes.

GIANT Sort of morning when it feels good to be alive. Isn't that so, Pete?

PETE (*gasping*) Yeah. Just go easy, Joe, go easy.

GIANT Beautiful morning. Course, they won't get mornings as good as this where this family is going, you know, kid.

DAVID They're going to Birmingham.

GIANT That's right. You're a bright lad.

DAVID I was top in maths last term.

GIANT I can tell... No, you don't get air like this in Birmingham, kid.

(He has stopped moving completely now and breathes in deeply, raising his end of the piano to chest height. This increased weight is too much for Pete who collapses and the piano crashes to the ground. We cannot see if he is injured. The

giant continues as if nothing were the matter.)

GIANT It's good when you're doing well at school, cheers your mother up. Got to keep the woman of the house happy, you know. I've always made a point of keeping the woman of the house happy. Er, is there a MR Bernard, kid?

DAVID He doesn't live here any more.

GIANT (*very interested*) Mm.

(*David is not taking much notice of him. He is straining to see if the little man is OK. Prompted, the giant also looks. The little man is safe but sobbing quietly to himself.*)

GIANT You OK, Pete? (*The only answer is a further flood of tears. The giant takes everything in his stride.*) I think it's time for a cup of tea. You want one, kid?

DAVID I don't drink tea.

GIANT Very wise. Let me give you a word of advice, kid, never take up the piano.

DAVID I play the euphonium in school.

GIANT I'm all in favour of these new sports they're introducing into the curriculum nowadays.

5 *The Bernards' hall by the entrance to the kitchen*

(*Everything is in a turmoil with packing cases and boxes everywhere. David seems at a loss for what to do. He eventually sees Mrs Bernard crawling around in a kitchen cupboard which she is doing her best to empty.*)

DAVID Mrs Bernard? I've come for Allen.

MRS B What?

DAVID I've come to call for Allen.

MRS B But we're moving house today, haven't you noticed?

(*As Mrs Bernard talks, David is fascinated to dis-*

cover that her voice travels along the line of kitchen base units and out through the gap where the cooker had been.)

DAVID Allen told me. Can he still come out to play, Mrs Bernard?

MRS B No, he jolly well can't!

DAVID Oh. Sorry, Mrs Bernard, I'll just go then. (*He is now peering into the cupboard so as to see Mrs Bernard. He is actually inside for some of the above conversation.*)

MRS B Are you in this cupboard with me, David?

DAVID Yes.

MRS B Mm.

(*She clambers out. David attempts to follow her.*)

MRS B Not so fast. You're younger than me. Start passing out all that stuff in there, will you. I can't reach half of it. There's things in there from when we first moved in here twelve years ago. (*Articles begin to emerge. She puts most in a rubbish bin, although the occasional item is placed in a packing case. We see only David's hand.*) Mung beans—I always meant to try those, never dared—haricot beans, lentils, bulgar wheat—BULGAR WHEAT!—the money I've wasted. No wonder this vegetarian food's so healthy, we never got to eat any of it. What's this? Dear me, that's what became of the egg slicer. And uh! I think that's the egg. I wonder what the expiry date is on this packet of dried prunes.... (*She reads it and immediately throws it in the bin.*) It's an antique.

(*This continues for some time. Suddenly there is a gasp from David from inside the cupboard. Mrs Bernard is quick to notice.*)

MRS B What's that, David?

DAVID I don't think you'll want this, Mrs Bernard.

MRS B I want everything in the cupboard, David.

DAVID Not this, Mrs Bernard.

MRS B Let me be the best judge of that, David.

DAVID But Mrs Bernard...

MRS B Hand it over, David.

DAVID Mrs Bernard.

MRS B HAND IT OVER!

DAVID Are you sure, Mrs Bernard?

MRS B Oh, I think so, David.

DAVID Don't say I didn't warn you, Mrs Bernard.

(*She reaches out to collect the object but jumps up with a shriek of disgust so suddenly that we fail to see just what it is. Pulling a face and looking away, as if the thing were too awful to contemplate, she gingerly places the object in the bin using a newspaper to hold it.*)

MRS B (*She is putting other rubbish on top to hide the mysterious object as she speaks*) What did you give that to me for? Uh! It's disgusting!

DAVID I warned you, Mrs Bernard.

MRS B Mm. I've had enough of the cupboards, David, you can get out now.

(*The two wash their hands in the sink scrubbing them vigorously. Mrs Bernard picks up a baby's bottle discovered at the bottom of the cupboard. She has a dreamy, faraway expression.*)

MRS B It's a long time since I needed those. Happy days, happy days.

DAVID Are you taking everything with you to Birmingham, Mrs Bernard?

MRS B Everything except Allen's father, I'm leaving him here.

DAVID Doesn't he mind being left behind?

MRS B (*After a long pause and a searching glance at David*) You came to say goodbye to Allen?

DAVID Yes.

MRS B I suppose I can spare him for an hour or so. He's not doing anything to help anyway.

DAVID Where is he?

MRS B In his bedroom. He's crying. We're leaving home, David, hadn't you realised?

DAVID Allen told me.

MRS B Be back at twelve at the latest. Twelve. You tell him from me. The latest, you hear.

GIANT (*arriving with two incredibly dirty and huge mugs*) Excuse me, love, do you mind if I wash the cups? I like to drink out of a clean cup wherever possible, on account of the germs see.

MRS B I can see that.

GIANT Got anything to scrape them out with? Ah, there'll be something in here.

(*He starts to rummage throught he rubbish bin. Mrs Bernard is very anxious.*)

MRS B I shouldn't think so, it's full of er...sharp things.

GIANT Shouldn't fuss over me, love, nothing in here's going to trouble a big fella like...uh! Oh dear oh dear oh dear, what's that doing in there?

(*He has grasped hold of the object discovered earlier by David. He shakes his hand as if he has just been bitten. We still can't make out what it is.*)

DAVID It's Mrs Bernard's!

MRS B All right, David, all right! It's very old.

GIANT Mm.

DAVID I found it at the bottom of the kitchen cupboard beside...

MRS B I think you'd better go and see Allen now.

(*The giant is vainly trying to rub his hand clean on his trousers, a sick expression on his face.*)

DAVID It wasn't mine.

MRS B Upstairs, David!

6 *The landing of the Bernards' house*

(*David is outside Allen's bedroom. Three notices are pinned to the door. 'PRIVATE: KEEP OUT' 'ON NO ACCOUNT ENTER' 'PLEASE KNOCK'. David totally ignores the signs and barges straight in.*)

7 *Allen's Bedroom*

DAVID You should have seen what was in your mother's kitchen cupboard. Uh, it was horrible!

(*Allen is lying on his bare mattress looking very sorry for himself. The bed itself has been dismantled ready for moving. He ignores David.*)

DAVID You upset?

ALLEN A bit.

DAVID Why?

ALLEN We're leaving home, haven't you noticed?

DAVID Yeah. Your mother told me. You upset because you're leaving your dad?

Allen My dad? Don't be stupid!

DAVID Your mother said we could go out till twelve. Coming?

ALLEN Suppose so.

(*He bursts into tears. David is dumbfounded.*)

DAVID Don't be stupid, Allen, you're leaving this morning.

ALLEN I'll never see her again.

DAVID 'Her'?

ALLEN Lucy-Ann Brown.

DAVID Lucy-Ann Brown! She's a girl!

ALLEN That's funny. With a name like that and all. I never noticed.

DAVID Yeah, but crying over a girl. A girl! I didn't even know you knew her, she's in my sets at school.

ALLEN Remember that game of kiss-chase we played in the school yard in Junior School?

DAVID Yeah, what of it?

ALLEN Lucy-Ann let me catch her.

DAVID Yeah, a few let me.

ALLEN Did they? Who?

DAVID Secret! So you're sad you're leaving this girl, er Lucy-Ann, behind?

ALLEN I wanna say goodbye to her.

DAVID But Allen…
ALLEN I wanna.
DAVID But Allen…
ALLEN Wanna.
DAVID Allen…
ALLEN Wanna!
DAVID We'll go see her then.

8 *The Bernards' kitchen*

(Mrs Bernard and the giant are sitting on the floor looking very cosy and sipping coffee from sparklingly clean mugs.)

GIANT I like Birmingham.

(The two boys enter and Mrs Bernard jumps up rather guiltily.)

MRS B This is my boy.
GIANT You don't look old enough.
ALLEN I'm twelve!
GIANT I meant your mum.
ALLEN Oh her, she's thirty-nine.
MRS B I'll see you later, darling.

9 *The Bernards' front drive*

(The little man is hauling the piano into the van. It is obviously too much for him on his own. Allen taps him on his shoulder causing him more trouble.)

ALLEN Take care with that piano. It's my mother's favourite.

(David's father is passing the house carrying his briefcase and wearing his work suit. He is looking totally fed up. The boys fall in alongside him as he walks to work.)

DAVID Hi, dad. You off to work?
MR H Er yes, I thought I'd catch up with a bit of paperwork, you know.
DAVID But it's a Saturday.

MR H Is it?

DAVID All day.

MR H Ah yes, a Saturday...

DAVID But you never work on Saturdays.

MR H No.

DAVID What are you walking for?

MR H Well I, er...

DAVID Has the car broken down again?

MR H Er no, your mother, er, decided to use it this morning.

DAVID But she can't drive!

MR H (*he has started to walk very quickly. The boys struggle to keep up*) Er no, she's er going to start to learn this morning.

DAVID But she's never shown any interest before.

MR H Er no er...Sorry boys (*he breaks away, almost running. He calls back over his shoulder*) I'll have to get off, lots to do. Hope you like Birmingham, Allen.

ALLEN Fancy learning to drive at your mother's age, she's nearly as old as my mum.

DAVID We're only twelve.

ALLEN So? What's that got to do with your mother taking up driving when she's absolutely ancient?

DAVID Nothing, I was thinking about you and Lucy-Ann. I mean, we're too young for girls. We'll grow into that when we're older, thirteen or fourteen or something, when we're really old.

ALLEN Grow up, David, will you. You know nothing. You're just a great big kid. Come on, race you to the end of the street. Last one there's a squashed tomato!

10 *Wasteland by a canal*

(We see a scrapyard, partly demolished factories, the blue haze of the nearby motorway fly-over, general debris. The boys run ecstatically by the

canal, kicking dandelions, nettles and rusty cans into the water as they go. Allen stops, taking in the view and breathing in the air as if it were pure countryside.)

ALLEN It'll be awful leaving here. Birmingham just can't have anything to compare with this.

11 *A light woodland walk*

(*It is the drive to the Browns' mansion. This scene contrasts markedly with that of the previous one. The boys are watching a dove cooing in the trees above.*)

ALLEN Nice here, isn't it?

DAVID Yeah. Reminds me of that Scout Camp we stayed at, in Wales last year, remember?

ALLEN Yeah. See that dove in the trees?

DAVID Yeah.

ALLEN Beautiful.

DAVID Yeah.

ALLEN Lovely things, doves.

DAVID Yeah.

ALLEN Symbol of peace, you know.

DAVID That so?

ALLEN Yeah. You could shoot it easy from here. They taste great, like chicken only more bones.

DAVID Lovely. You know, her dad must be worth a bomb living here.

ALLEN He was a singer.

DAVID Was he? I've never heard of him.

ALLEN Johnny Brown.

DAVID Still never heard of him. Has he ever been on TV?

ALLEN Dunno. Lucy-Ann says they play him a lot on Radio Two.

DAVID Is he dead?

ALLEN 'Course he's not dead.

DAVID Thought you have to be dead to get on Radio Two.

ALLEN Her mother's a dentist.

DAVID Aw, tough luck.

(They ring the bell at the over-ornate front door. It plays a tune, the first few bars of 'There's no business like show business...' Johnny Brown is very tanned and has a loud sports shirt open to the waist, revealing an incredibly hairy chest. He is wearing lots of jewellery and a particularly flashy medallion.)

MR BROWN Hi, kids. Lucy-Ann's out, I'm afraid, she'll be finishing at the beauty salon about now. I'm expecting her back any moment. Course, she may have stopped on for a facial, you know what women are like.

ALLEN Yeah! Er, can I leave a message?

MR BROWN Sure, fire away, kid.

ALLEN Er, tell her Al called to er say goodbye and that he'll er be leaving this morning but er that he'll er keep in touch and er write.

MR BROWN Leaving are you, kid? Where are you heading?

ALLEN Er Birmingham.

MR BROWN Aw, tough luck. Played at Birmingham, mind you, once or twice, in the old days, you know. *(He poses a bit.)*

ALLEN Great!

(Johnny Brown waits expectantly for David to say something too. The boy is dazzled by all the conspicuous riches of the house and the fact that the sun is being reflected in his eyes by the medallion. He obviously has not heard what Johnny Brown has been talking about.)

DAVID Birmingham? Er, you've played there, er sorry, I don't play football myself.

(A long silence as they try and puzzle out what David is on about.)

ALLEN We'll go now.

MR BROWN *(breaking out into loud laughter)* Very good, that's very good, kid, yes very good, ha ha, 'I don't play football myself!' very good.

(Everyone now breaks into laughter: David without in the slightest knowing why, Allen because it's expected of him.)

MR BROWN You're not going to Birmingham are you kid?

DAVID No, I'm staying here.

MR BROWN Super! You'll have to keep in touch. Come and call on Lucy-Ann some time, stay for eats, what d'ya say, kid?

DAVID Great!

12 *The banks of the canal*

(The two boys are sitting silently by a lock. David is throwing stones absent–mindedly into the lock, Allen is stripping dandelions and squeezing them into a gooey mess.

DAVID Something wrong?

ALLEN *(eventually, as if he's been working out how to ask the question)* When I'm gone, who will you hang around with?

DAVID Dunno. There's always Matthew Wilder.

ALLEN Wilder?

DAVID I've got to have someone, haven't I.

ALLEN Yeah, but not Wilder, he's a donkey!

DAVID He's in the school football team.

ALLEN I'M in the school football team. What is it with you and this football team business anyway? You're always on about it. You made a complete fool of yourself back there.

DAVID I want to get in the team when you leave.

ALLEN You? You're useless, you play like a powder puff.

(This time it is David's turn to be quiet. He throws more stones in the lock, Allen throws in the crushed dandelion and joins in with more stones and bits of glass, rubbish etc.)

ALLEN Do you think you'll see anything of Lucy-Ann when I'm gone?

DAVID She's in my class isn't she, I'm bound to see

her.

ALLEN Yeah. Suppose so. So you won't be going round to her house for tea like her dad said?

DAVID Course not!

(*As the two boys have been talking a barge has gradually been rising into view as the water level in the lock changes. There are bits of rubbish all over it and the man at the helm is holding the crushed up dandelion.*)

BARGEE Clear off you two! Take up darts if you want to throw things.

ALLEN (*pretending he has not heard*) Did you hear something?

BARGEE You two deaf or what? I told you to clear off. Or do I have to get off this barge and give you a thumping.

ALLEN You and whose army! You old duffer, go get your pension, you couldn't catch a cold!

BARGEE What did you say?

ALLEN I said, you old duffer, that you couldn't catch a cold in an igloo.

BARGEE I won't have to catch you, son.

ALLEN Yeah!

BARGEE Yeah. Geoffrey, toss that little twerp into the water for me will you.

(*Close-up of Geoffrey. He is every bit as huge as the giant but with a halting way of speaking and a great beard. He is very slow but has crept up unawares and grabbed hold of the two boys by the scruff of their necks.*)

GEOFFREY Which one, uncle?

BARGEE The skinny one with the spots.

(*There is a scream from Allen and an audible sigh of relief from David.*)

GEOFFREY Do I duff him up first, uncle?

BARGEE Na, just toss him into the canal!

GEOFFREY Right, uncle.

(*Allen is dangled like a worm on a hook over the filthy water of the canal. Geoffrey suddenly looks as if he might be having second thoughts.)*

GEOFFREY Uncle, are you sure I can't duff him up, just a little bit, rip off an arm or a leg or his head or something, just a bit of fun, eh? I do like a bit of fun. Go on uncle, a spot of GBH, what do you say, eh?

BARGEE (*like he's announcing the death sentence*) The water!

(*There is a loud piercing scream from Allen, David hides his eyes. We see the look of amazement on Geoffrey's face as he looks down.*)

GEOFFREY Uh! Missed!

(*Allen has landed on the edge of the bank and is lying still, frozen with fear. David darts forward and pulls him to his feet. Allen's legs have turned to jelly.*)

DAVID Get up! Get up! Run!

(*They escape. The two men watch them go and then break out into hysterical laughter.*)

BARGEE Missed! (*More laughter.*)

13 *Another part of the canal bank*

DAVID I think we got away. You OK?

ALLEN Take me back to mummy, David. I nearly died, I nearly died!

DAVID Don't cry, Allen, I hate it when you cry.

ALLEN What do you expect me to do, laugh? I nearly died.

DAVID You're all right, aren't you?

ALLEN Oh, I'm great, I'm great. My legs have turned to jelly, my face is all numb, I've got flashing lights in my head, stomach pains, cramp in my shoulders and nausea and a wrenched elbow and vertigo and back-ache and dizziness and high blood pressure and nervous exhaustion and my ankles are all swollen where that monster dangled me upside down, my nerves are all in shreds, and...

Mm

DAVID Yeah, but you're all right apart from that, aren't you?

14 *The front of the Bernards' house*

(The little removal man is struggling to carry a washing machine into the van. David and Allen arrive. Allen is in a terrible state and is being supported by his friend. Allen knocks Pete to one side in his desperation to get in the house.)

ALLEN Out of my way!

(Mrs Bernard is busily loading the boot of her car with suitcases. Making no attempt to help her, the giant is leaning against the car. It is clear they have struck up a relationship during the time the boys have been away.)

GIANT You'll need a man to help you with all the heavy work when you get to Birmingham, when you're settling into your new house, you know.

MRS B I've got a man.

GIANT Who?

MRS B Why, Allen of course.

(They watch as the wretched Allen is helped into the house by David.)

GIANT You could have problems there.

MRS B David? David? What on earth has happened?

DAVID Er...Allen has had a bit of a shock, by the canal. He er...nearly fell in.

MRS B In the canal? He could have drowned.

GIANT Polluted to death.

MRS B I've warned him about that canal.

GIANT Funny that, my kid brother works on a barge on that stretch of the canal, temporary job for the summer, he's a student.

DAVID On a scrap metal barge?

GIANT Yeah.

DAVID Is he as big as you?

GIANT Yeah.

DAVID With big hairy arms?

GIANT Yeah.

DAVID And does he have red eyes, a beard and talk with a deep deep voice?

GIANT Yeah, that's our kid! You know him then?

DAVID Never seen him before in my life! (*He runs inside.*)

GIANT I can see why you're moving.

15 *Allen's Bedroom*

ALLEN I could have been killed, killed, do you hear me, KILLED!

DAVID I think it was a joke.

ALLEN You think I don't know a joke when I see one? A madman? He was a killer, I'm telling you, a monster, if I hadn't have got us away when I did we'd both have been a gonner, he was eight foot tall.

DAVID He's the brother of the removal man, he just told me.

(*Allen is startled and darts to the window. Below them the little man is once again struggling, this time with a huge armchair. The giant is ambling along with a tiny cushion.*)

ALLEN Which one? Which one is the brother?

DAVID The giant!

ALLEN I feel ill.

DAVID Do you want a glass of water?

ALLEN Something stronger.

DAVID I know just the thing, I saw it in the kitchen.

ALLEN Anything. I need something to perk me up.

DAVID This stuff will do that, all right.

16 *The Bernards' kitchen*

(*David is looking in the rubbish bin. He sees the object which so upset the giant and pulls a face. Then he seizes something.*)

DAVID (*delighted expression*) That's the stuff to cure Allen.

17 *Allen's bedroom*

ALLEN Tastes lovely, what is it?
DAVID Gripe Water.
ALLEN GRIPE WATER!

18 *The Bernards' hall*

(*Lucy-Ann is admiring the giant's muscles.*)
LUCY-ANN I bet you're incredibly strong.
GIANT Lots of exercise, love, and clean living. My mate now, the little fellow outside…
LUCY-ANN The scrawny one lifting the tumble–drier into the van?
GIANT That's the fellow. Now he doesn't take care of his body.
LUCY-ANN Too little exercise?
GIANT Too much. He doesn't know how to pace himself.
LUCY-ANN Do you work out in the gym?
GIANT Sort of.
LUCY-ANN I think it's nice when a man takes such good care of his body. Good looks run in my family, you know, my father is a Radio Two pop idol.
GIANT Is that so. You've got to be good-looking to appear on Radio. What's your father called?
LUCY-ANN His stage name's Johnny Brown, his real name too. He's a singer.
GIANT Did he sing that song about a body rotting in a grave?
LUCY-ANN He most certainly did not!
(*Mrs Bernard comes in. She has been helping the little man load up the van and is obviously weary.*)
MRS B That's about it. Oh hello, Lucy-Ann.
LUCY-ANN Hello, Mrs Bernard. We were just discussing

Joe's body. I was just saying what a magnificent physique he has.

MRS B Mm, he has, I suppose. I hadn't noticed myself. How old are you, Lucy-Ann?

LUCY-ANN Twelve, nearly thirteen, I'm very tall for my age.

MRS B I can see you're very forward. Have you come to say goodbye to Allen?

LUCY-ANN I think I should, don't you, Mrs Bernard.

MRS B Oh I think so, Lucy-Ann.

DAVID (*he has been on the stairs for some time although the others have not seen him*) He's not feeling well, Mrs Bernard.

LUCY-ANN Heart-broken at leaving me?

MRS B (*quickly*) Fell in the canal!

DAVID Well, neither actually, He can't stop...er... burping. He's been drinking er gripe water.

MRS B GRIPE WATER!

LUCY-ANN GRIPE WATER!

DAVID It was in the kitchen cupboards beside that thing I found there, you know, the...

MRS B You've said quite enough already!

(*There is a commotion on the landing. Allen stumbles towards the stairs. He is drunk.*)

MRS B There's alcohol in gripe water. How much did he drink?

DAVID A bottle.

MRS B The whole bottle?

DAVID Yes.

(*They are interrupted by a burst of awful singing from Allen.*)

ALLEN I'm forever blowing bubbulsh, pretty bubbulsh in the air. Mummy, I think I can fly—wheeee!

(*He makes an attempt to jump. At the last moment he clings on precariously to the stair rail. Mrs Bernard sprints up the stairs where she struggles to save him from falling.*)

MRS B Allen, Allen, hold on my baby, mummy's

coming.

ALLEN (*seeing the girl*) Looshy, Looshy my darling, youf come for me.

LUCY-ANN (*disgustedly turning away*) If there's one thing I can't stand, it's a man who is unable to take his drink! Come along, David, take me away from this house.

DAVID What?

LUCY-ANN I'm waiting, David.

DAVID Me? You're waiting for me?

LUCY-ANN (*standing by the door and tapping her foot impatiently*) I'm not used to being kept waiting, David.

DAVID Yes...right, er sorry Mrs Bernard.

(*As the boy rather dazedly follows her the giant points to where Mrs Bernard is fighting a losing battle to save her son from falling down the stairs.*)

GIANT That boy needs a father! (*Raising his voice but making no attempt to help*) Carry him down, Mrs Bernard, carry him down!

19 *Outside the Bernards' house*

(*David is hurrying after Lucy-Ann. The little man is struggling with a rolled–up carpet. We can hear Allen's anguished voice.*)

ALLEN Looshy, Looshy, don't leave me, Looshy! I'm shorry Looshy, shorry...

20 *The Bernards' hall. A few minutes later*

GIANT I will not have you driving the car with a drunken child in it. What would happen if he was ill on the motorway?

MRS B Well...I don't know really.

GIANT You know very well. No, there's only one thing for it, er, Mrs...?

MRS B Hilary, my name's Hilary.

GIANT There's only one thing for it, er Hilary, you, me and the boy will have to travel by car. The little fellow can drive the van. He should be able to manage without me for once.

(*At this moment the little man is single-handedly hauling out a bookcase.*)

GIANT As I was saying, we can't risk you being distracted on the M6 motorway by a sick boy. I'll look after him, don't you worry.

ALLEN (*he is at the top of the stairs looking down at the pair*) Mum, mum, I feel awful.

GIANT Haven't you caused your mother enough heart-ache for one day?

ALLEN But I feel awful, honest, I just...(*He looks ill.*)

MRS B Allen...Allen...are you all right?

ALLEN I think, I think...

MRS B Yes?

GIANT What is it, boy, come on, spit it out!

ALLEN I think I'm going to be sick.

(*He IS sick—over the banisters and down to the hall below! There is a stunned silence.*)

MRS B Oh Allen, look what you've done.

GIANT He's travelling in the van! With the little fellow!

21 *The Street*

(*David and Lucy-Ann watch the van and the car prepare to set off. The giant is crammed into the front passenger seat of Mrs Bernard's small car. Allen is in the front seat of the removal van.)*

LUCY-ANN You made father laugh.

DAVID I try to stay cheerful.

LUCY-ANN Something about football, I think it was, I didn't understand properly.

(*As she is speaking the car draws off. Mrs Bernard gives them a curt nod, the giant winks at the boy and blows a kiss to the girl.)*

DAVID Neither did I.

LUCY-ANN You ARE funny.

ALLEN (*he too is drawing away, but waving frantically to attract their attention; Lucy-Ann is conspicuously ignoring him and David's attention is on the girl*) Bye, goodbye.

DAVID Mm.

ALLEN Bye Davy...Lucy-Ann...bye...

DAVID (*remembering to wave*) Oh, yeah, bye.

LUCY-ANN (*far too softly for Allen to hear*) Cheerio, Al.

(*Matthew too has been watching Allen leave. He dismounts from his bike and falls into line beside David and Lucy-Ann.*)

MATTHEW Hi, David, hi, Lucy-Ann.

LUCY-ANN (*ignoring him*) Father said something about inviting you to tea, Davy.

DAVID Yeah.

MATTHEW I like beer myself.

LUCY-ANN Who's your fat friend?

(*Crushed, Matthew cycles off without another word.*)

DAVID It's Matthew Wilder, he's in our class, you must know him.

LUCY-ANN (*very sharply*) Of course I know him! (*Softer now*) Oh, Davy, sometimes you're such a boy.

DAVID Matthew and me are rivals to get in the school soccer team when we go back. Matthew's a real hard tackler.

LUCY-ANN I can see that. I hate sports people.

DAVID Do you?

LUCY-ANN Loathe them!

DAVID I'm no good at playing sports really, I've always wanted to be, but I'm slow and hopeless.

LUCY-ANN Oh I know that.

DAVID You do?

LUCY-ANN Of course, everyone knows it, Mr Dalglish told us in Geography; you play like a powder puff.

DAVID I told you I was hopeless.

LUCY-ANN You're a musician, Davy. Musicians are very sensitive people. And don't forget, I've heard you play the euphonium in assembly.

DAVID Have you?

LUCY-ANN Yes I have, you play beautifully. My father says the euphonium is a much under-rated instrument. He's a musician, you know, on Radio Two a lot.

DAVID Great! I listen to Radio Two all the time.

LUCY-ANN What's your favourite programme?

DAVID Oh, it's all good. I think I've heard your dad; he's awfully talented.

LUCY-ANN (*pleased*) Have you ever played kiss-chase?

DAVID Mm.

LUCY-ANN What does that mean?

DAVID Just 'Mm' I suppose, dunno really.

(*She smiles and they walk along the road which is bathed in romantic sunlight.*)

DAVID You should have seen what Allen's mother had at the bottom of her kitchen cupboard. It was disgusting!

LUCY-ANN What was it?

DAVID (*noticing that Matthew is attempting to see and hear, he moves very close*) I'll have to whisper.

LUCY-ANN Oh that is disgusting! Uh! But I'm glad you told me, Davy, because there's to be no secrets between us from this day forward. We're kindred spirits you and I.

DAVID I told you it was disgusting.

MATTHEW What are you two talking about?

LUCY-ANN What's it got to do with you, fatty!

DAVID (*as Matthew recoils*) You're too young, Matthew. (*Kindly*) It's all right, I'll tell you sometime.

LUCY-ANN Go pump your tyres, fat man, you've got a leak!

(*Matthew cycles off, defeated.*)

LUCY-ANN I'm not very good at running either, you know, Davy.

DAVID How do you mean?

LUCY-ANN I mean when I play kiss-chase.

Mm

DAVID Sorry?

LUCY-ANN I'm always getting caught...and kissed, Davy.

DAVID Mm.

(A car drives down the road, veering wildly from side to side. It is David's mother and father. There are L plates on the car. Mrs Hannigan is driving.)

DAVID It's my mum and dad. It's the first time she's ever driven a car. I thought my dad was at work.

MRS H *(winding down window)* They've moved then.

DAVID Just gone. This is Lucy-Ann Brown.

LUCY-ANN Hello, Mrs Hannigan, Mr Hannigan.

MRS H I know your dad, gorgeous singer, very manly.

LUCY-ANN Well thank you, Mrs Hannigan. Are you enjoying being a driving instructor, Mr Hannigan?

MR H Mm.

MRS H I've warned you about that!

(They roar off with much screeching of gears and nearly crash into Matthew Wilder who has ventured onto the road. Mrs Hannigan shouts at him from the car.)

MRS H Get off the road, fatty!

(Lucy-Ann watches the car make its uneasy way down the road.)

LUCY-ANN I like you mum, she's got style.

DAVID Mm.

LUCY-ANN Know something?

DAVID What?

LUCY-ANN I love it when you say that.

DAVID What?

LUCY-ANN "Mm"

DAVID "Mm"?

LUCY-ANN "Mm"

DAVID Why?

LUCY-ANN It's...well...lovely, expressive, you know.

DAVID Do you think so?

LUCY-ANN When you say it, it is.

DAVID Great.

LUCY-ANN Say it again for me, Davy, please.

DAVID Mm.

LUCY-ANN Again.

DAVID Mm.

LUCY-ANN It's a lovely word, so...expressive. You can hold my hand if you like. If you want to that is.

DAVID I do. It's just that I've never held a girl's hand before, in public, you know...

LUCY-ANN (*holding his hand*) There. That didn't hurt did it?

DAVID No.

(*They walk off into the sunlight. They are moving away from the camera.*)

LUCY-ANN You've got musician's hands, all soft and smooth, like a boy's.

DAVID I am a boy.

LUCY Mm.

DAVID YOU'RE at it now, you've just said it.

LUCY-ANN You see the effect you're having on me, Davy.

DAVID Mm.

LUCY-ANN Can anyone join in?

DAVID Mmmmm.

(*She joins in. They both laugh and continue humming. The barge is making its way along the canal. The giant bargee is sitting lazily at the front.*)

DAVID (*noticing the barge*) Oh no!

(*He runs away. Lucy-Ann catches him up and puts her arm around him.*)

LUCY-ANN I'll look after you, Davy, don't worry.

DAVID Mm.

LUCY-ANN Calm down. And, Davy, you've used that word quite enough already. You can overdo a good line, you know.

IAN LUMSDEN

Personal Essay

I had this fantastic idea for a story. I'm always having fantastic ideas for stories. Trouble is I never get to write them. Briefly, the story was to be about two young boys who meet up on the day that one of them is to move house. They would then have a 'battle' with a rival gang and win. Their victory was to be short-lived however, for shortly afterwards one of the boys was to set off into the sunset and the one left behind was to appreciate the meaning of goodbye. The story was to end with the reappearance of the gang. I can almost see it in print now. Almost. Oh dear, just another in the long line of great stories I never got to write.

I did start that story. I got as far as David choking on his breakfast. Trouble is his mother noticed, and Mrs Hannigan, a woman who chews girders, was born. Before I knew what was happening a perfectly good story that would, I assure you, have brought tears to the eyes, had been hijacked and turned into a comedy. The story was finished all right, but it was not the one I had intended writing. Matthew Wilder is the sole survivor of my intended rival gang and what a terrifying character he turned out to be. True, Allen Bernard did leave home but far from leaving a lump in David's throat as he waves a last goodbye to his rapidly departing best mate, the poor chump scarcely notices, so taken up is he by Lucy-Ann Brown.

Ah, Lucy-Ann. Lucy-Ann Brown. I don't know where she came from. One moment I had poor Allen crying in his bedroom, the next I found myself writing about a girl who let herself be caught playing kiss-chase in the Junior School playground. I don't know where she came from. I have a memory of playing kiss-chase in the playground—we called it kissy-catchy and there are, I know, lots of variations on the name. But I was the one no-one wanted to kiss and the girls all ran a lot faster than I could. I'd remember a Lucy-Ann if she'd allowed me to catch her, and I've no memory of that. But once I'd mentioned her she took over. And the name? That was my class at school who, having listened to the story, thought 'Susan' too humdrum a name. She had to be hyphenated, they said...Sarah-Jane, Penelope-Jane, Elizabeth-Ann, Lucy-Ann... that's the one, Sir, Lucy-Ann.

So what is true in the story? Very little, I'm afraid. *Mm* was not based on memory. I tended to think visually when I was writing: the little man doing all the work, the medallion around Johnny Brown's neck, the barge gradually rising into view from the lock, the professionally lacquered ringlets of Lucy-Ann, Mrs Bernard in the kitchen cupboard. I suppose, come to think of it, that her cupboards do have some foundation in fact. I have found some revoltingly awful things lost in the dim recesses of our cupboards. Our kitchen units are so designed that it is impossible to reach the corners. Things disappear rather like dirty dishes at the Mad Hatter's tea party.

Not true also is my abuse of gripe water. I'm reliably informed that you would have to drink an awful lot of the stuff before you would start to swing from the bannister. 'Poetic license' is what it is called.

I've referred to a story. Of course you know it as a play. I was editing an anthology of plays and suddenly I got this overwhelming urge to write one myself. I've written plays before but always for the stage. *Mm* was something I wanted to develop further, so I did. Yet its visual qualities seemed to cry out for filming and that dictated the final form.

All my material is typed into a word-processor. Changing a story into a play was not such a daunting task as it might appear, given that a lot of this particular story was dialogue in any case. I have these control buttons on my machine that delete, copy, exchange, format and so on almost instantly. If I type in, say, 'qqq' I can change that throughout the play for 'Mrs Hannigan:' with the maximum of speed and the minimum of typing skill. I love my word-processor!

What I did find difficult was in deciding what to leave out. Some of the funniest moments in the story were difficult to get into the script. For instance, when David leaves his parents to fight it out over the breakfast table the story has the line, 'He hated to see his father scream.' Strangely enough, that line works when classes read the story. But you'll not find it in the play. And I'm sure you're very grateful for that!

And David? Is David Hannigan a thinly disguised twelve year old Ian Lumsden who got the girl at the end of the story? No. Not on your life. I was Matthew Wilder!

RONY ROBINSON

Naughty Girls

CHARACTERS

MISS GRINDLE
JANICE
MARY
ANGELA
ROSE
HE
SHE
GLYNIS
CYNTHIA
MAVIS
DEIRDRE
LARRY
BARRY
DJ
HEADMASTER
INSPECTOR
MR O'SHEA
ANNOUNCER
FIREMEN

The play is set in Miss Grindle's classroom.

(*Girls doing wild animal impressions.*

GRINDLE Girls. You're like wild animals. And the inspector's coming today.

JANICE Tickets please.

GRINDLE The school inspector, to inspect you. Quiet. How many more times do I need to ask you.

MARY I don't know, Miss. How many more times *do* you need to ask us?

GRINDLE You will be in trouble, Mary. Mark my words.

ANGELA Three out of ten, Miss.

GRINDLE Quiet. Are you listening? What did I just say, Rose?

ROSE 'What did I just say Rose'.

GRINDLE Quiet. The inspector's coming. If you are not very very good I shall not let you listen to the educational play on the radio.

GIRLS Hurrah.

GRINDLE Be absolutely silent. Absolutely. Silent. Good. I'll tune us in.

(*Radio switched on. Tuning noises.*)

SHE Darling!

HE Darling!

SHE Darling!

HE Darling!

SHE Darling!

HE People might be listening darling!

SHE Who cares Darl—

(*Radio being retuned.*)

GIRLS Oh, Miss!

GRINDLE Never mind 'Oh Missing' me. We want the educational play and a nice quiet lesson for the inspector. Let's try this.

ANNOUNCER Good afternoon, children. Are you sitting comfortably? Then I'll begin.

ROSE I'm not sitting comfortably.

ANNOUNCER I hope I did not hear a child trying to be clever with me. But if I did or even if I didn't it's time for me to take a break for the adverts to persuade you to buy things you don't want with money you haven't got.

LARRY Socko socko socko socko!

SHE I don't know what to give him tonight. I've tried everything.

LARRY But she hasn't tried Socko's sausages has she?

SHE I wonder what he'd like?

BARRY Sausages!

SHE Sausages? No!

LARRY Not any old sausages. Socko's *new* sausages!

SHE Socko's sausages. 'The sausage that swells'. I'll try them, but they look very ordinary.

LARRY They aren't ordinary.

BARRY Not Socko's.

LARRY Listen to them fry.

SHE I hope he likes them. Here he comes. Tired and hungry enough to eat a horse 'till the cows come home.

LARRY A hungry man.

BARRY Meets his sausage.

HE Hello, darling. I could eat a horse till the cows come home.

SHE It's sausages tonight, darling.

HE Not sausages.

LARRY Not just sausages.

HE Well let me try them. Mmmm. Mmmm. They're very nice, darling. And what does it say here in the stripes? 'Socko's Sausages Are Charming'. Darling!

SHE Darling!

HE Darling!

SHE Darling!

(*Radio being retuned.*)

GIRLS Oh, Miss!

GRINDLE There's nothing very educational about that. I'm not letting you girls listen to that gutter talk. This might be it.

DJ Woeweeee and howsaboutthat? A ravefromthe-grave,kidsandkiddykins. Howeeee and righton-daddyo,Ishouldbiteabanana.Ha hee andnowa-dedicationanditsthelatestsmasheroo—

(*Radio being retuned.*)

GIRLS Oh, Miss!

GRINDLE It sounds like a foreign language and we do not want that. If we cannot find an educational play on the radio we shall have to make up one of our own. The inspector will be here at any moment.

GLYNIS Can we do a murder one, Miss?

MARY Oh yes, Miss. And you can be in it too, Miss.

CYNTHIA You can be the blood, Miss.

MAVIS Oh yes, Miss. Let's do a bloody play.

GRINDLE Girls, girls. We are going to do a *radio* play. A sound play. So I shall not need to be the blood. You cannot see on radio. What a silly girl Cynthia is, isn't she girls?

GIRLS No, Miss.

GRINDLE When you do a radio play you make up the sounds. They don't have to be real sounds. In fact real sounds don't sound real.

ROSE She's going again.

MARY It's a bit early in the lesson isn't it?

GRINDLE Real blood doesn't make a noise. But radio blood would sound like this.
(*The sound of radio blood.*)

DEIRDRE That sounds like my mum's plumbing.

CYNTHIA Question, Miss!

GRINDLE Yes, Cynthia? Always ask questions when you don't understand. Probe and learn. Ask your questions, especially when the inspector calls.

MAVIS We could call the murder play that, Miss.

CYNTHIA Why are your teeth like stars, Miss?

GRINDLE I don't know, Mavis. Why are my teeth like stars?

CYNTHIA Because they come out at night. Ow, Rose. Stop pinching me.

ROSE You stop pinching old jokes then.

GLYNIS Yes, Cynthia, we want to do a play with blood.

JANICE We could do Macbreath, Miss.

ANGELA If you're not too windy, Miss.

MARY Let's do something romantic, Miss.

GLYNIS Oh yes, Miss. I could go 'Darling'.

DEIRDRE And I could go 'Darling'.

GLYNIS 'Darling'.

MAVIS And I could stick a Socko Sausage up your nose.

GLYNIS Ow, Mavis!

GRINDLE Stop I won't have fighting. I don't believe in violence. I will smack you if you don't stop sticking sausages up each others' noses.

MAVIS It's only a radio play, Miss. We're only pretending sausages and noses.

GLYNIS And blood coming down noses, Miss. Let's have your sound effect.

DEIRDRE Darling!

GLYNIS Darling.

GRINDLE Girls. Stop. The inspector will be here soon and I shall be in terrible trouble.

JANICE My sister got in trouble with an inspector, Miss.

GRINDLE Was she a teacher, Janice?

JANICE No, Miss, she hadn't paid her bus fare. Ow, Rose. Stop pinching me.

ROSE Stop pinching old jokes, let's have the play.

ANGELA Let's make it sad as well, Miss.

MARY Yes, Miss, plenty of waterworks.

DEIRDRE And we want some boys in it, Miss. I'll just go and get some.

GRINDLE Sit down, Deidre. We're pretending.

DEIRDRE It's not the same pretending boys, Miss.

JANICE Can we pretend anything, Miss?

GRINDLE Anything at all! That is the beauty of radio.

JANICE I'm going to pretend to be a milkman, Miss. They're always exciting.

ROSE Me too, in a deep voice. Morning, Miss Grindle, what can I do for you? Two yoghurts and how's your father?

DEIRDRE Darling!

ROSE Darling!

MARY Good morning milkman. It's a lovely day isn't it?

ROSE Yes.

JANICE No it's not. It's raining. Listen. Sssssss

MAVIS That's not rain. That's a snake. Look out milkman.

CYNTHIA And there's a tiger too. Listen. Grrrrrrrrr.

DEIRDRE Quick, milkman. He's after your yoghurts.

GRINDLE Stop this silliness girls. Whoever heard of a tiger biting a milkman? The inspector will be here any minute and—

(*Knocks at a door. The door opens.*)

HEAD Good morning, Miss Grindle, girls.

GRINDLE Good morning, headmaster!

GIRLS Good morning, headmaster!

CYNTHIA Grrrrrrrr, headmaster!

HEAD Miss Grindle, this is Mr McChoakumchild, the school inspector. He has come to inspect you.

INS Thank you for introducing me, head hampster.

HEAD Headm— 'head hampster', Miss Grindle.

GRINDLE Yes head hampster.

HEAD Now, Miss Grindle, I am sure there is some perfectly acceptable reason for Cynthia to be crawling about on the floor making grrrrrrr noises on the day the inspector calls?

GRINDLE We're doing a play, head hampster.

INS Oh super. I love plays. And who are you, little girl?

ROSE (*in her deep voice*) Knock it orf, mate. That's out of order, right?

GRINDLE Rose.

ROSE I'm only acting up. It's playtime and I'm a milkman.

INS How imaginative. And what has happened in the play so far?

MARY The milkman has just called.

JANICE And Miss Grindle is going to be the blood.

GLYNIS Do it for him now, Miss!

GRINDLE No!

ANGELA She's shy, Mr Inspector. You ask her!

INS I will, I will. There's no need to be shy with these lovely girls, Miss Shingle. And I am only an inspector with the power of sacking you on the spot if you don't come up to scratch. And what are you doing little girl?

GLYNIS Coming up to scratch. On the spot sir.

INS What a lovely imaginative class. Such fun. And you're shy with them, Miss Pringle! I insist you show us your blood.

HEAD (*aside*) And so do I. The inspector is the power and glory of the education system. I'm not spending the last few years of my professional life in this madhouse with you. I want a nice quiet school in the posh end of town. Get acting. (*Aloud*) Miss Pringle is ready to be the blood now, inspector.

INS About time too, head hampster.

HEAD Blood.

(*The sound of radio blood.*)

INS Terrible. It sounds like my mum's plumbing.

JANICE Please sir?

INS Yes, little girl? Ask your questions. Young citizens of tomorrow should always be encouraged to ask questions, Miss Fumble.

JANICE What's black and goes bounce bounce bounce?

INS That's a very interesting problem. I don't know. What is black and goes bounce bounce bounce?

JANICE A vicar on a trampoline. Ow, Rose.

INS Oh what lovely lovely girls. And what a lovely play. Carry on please.

(*A knock and a door opening.*)

O'SHEA Excuse me interrupting Headmaster.

HEAD (*aside*) Call me head *hamp*ster today, O'Shea. And don't swear. This man's an inspector.

O'SHEA I don't care if he's a superintendant. One of these naughty naughty girls has unscrewed the taps in the Doings. The corridors are flooded. And it's getting worse.

HEAD Ha ha ha, a good joke. Mr O'Shea our Welsh caretaker, this is Mr McChoakumchild, the powerful and glorious inspector.

INS Thank you, head hampster.

DEIRDRE You can be in our play, Mr O'Shea. You could pretend to be a grumpy school caretaker with no sense of how imaginative schoolgirls can be.

MAVIS Oh how charming. Ow, girls.

INS Oh yes, head hampster. Let's have him in it too.

ROSE How many pints today, Mr O'Shea?

CYNTHIA Mind the tiger, Mr O'Shea. Grrrrrrrrr.

GRINDLE Girls, stop.

HEAD Yes stop at once.

INS Stop this lovely play, Miss Grumble? These girls are living poetry! Stop??

GRINDLE Don't stop.

CYNTHIA Grrrrrrrr.

O'SHEA Get off! Off! Look what they've done. There's spit on my best trousers.

INS Oh carry on. I'm shutting my eyes to imagine better. I hope you are too, head hampster.

HEAD I am. And I hope you are too, Miss Grumble.

DEIRDRE If the tiger's bitten the caretaker, we shall need some blood.

O'SHEA Blood? In my day children knew their places. Get off my trousers, will you!

DEIRDRE It's only the sound of blood we need, Mr O'Shea.

O'SHEA You're not having the sound of mine. I've told you about the flooding in the Doings. I'm off. Goodbye.

ROSE Goodbye caretaker, take care.

INS What marvellous acting!

HEAD It is. I'm keeping my eyes shut too.

GRINDLE My feet are getting wet, head hampster.

HEADMASTER Make your blood noise!

(*The sound of radio blood.*)

ROSE I can hear something girls.

DEIRDRE It sounds like yesterday's school dinner.

HEAD Yes it does, Miss Grumble, try harder.

CYNTHIA I'm a tiger called Dracula the Second and I'm going to suck your blood, Miss Grumble. Grrrrrr

GRINDLE Get off!

INS It's wonderful what children can do with their imaginations head hampster!

HEAD Wonderful, sir.

INS If only more schools gave them this sort of creative context and experience it would be a better world tomorrow, don't you agree head hampster?

HEAD Very much so, sir.

INS If only all the teachers great and small would really join in and be part of the imaginative world of the young, don't you agree head hampster?

HEAD I do, sir. Girls, I wonder if I could have a small part in your play?

ANGELA Something small.

MAVIS A rat.

MARY Or a baby.

HEAD I think a baby. That would stretch me, girls.

ANGELA Well, it's raining.

JANICE Sssssssssssss.

ANGELA And the baby's out in the rain, crying.

HEAD Like this girls? Though I may be a bit rusty!

DEIRDRE You will be soon.

HEAD Baaaaaaaa. Goooooooooo. Ga ga...Gooooooee-eeeeeeeeeeoooooooooeee.

GIRLS That was very good, head hampster.

INS It was. Keep your eyes shut, head hampster. Like me. And imagine. In fact I can almost feel that rain and those baby's tears on the floor, slowly rising up my legs.

HEAD So can I, sir. Baaaa. Gooooooooooo.

JANICE Sssssssss. (*Aside*) Get up on the desks out of the flood, girls.

INS Oh a flood now! How clever and poetic and imaginative.

HEAD I can feel the waters rising sir, by keeping my eyes closed and joining in.

GRINDLE Head hampster, the water's nearly up to my knees.

HEAD Quiet, Grimhead, I'm trying to be a baby.

INS Carry on, girls. Don't be put off by the jealous older generation who dare not enter your charming world of fancy.

ROSE Fancy!

MAVIS Charming! Ow.

(*Distant bell of a fire engine.*)

GLYNIS I can hear a fire engine!

GIRLS So can we, girls!

INS So can I, girls! What a wonderful world of pretend. You make me believe I am wading through a new born baby's tears.

HEAD Baaaaa. Gooooo.

INS You make me hear a fire engine.

HEAD Baaaaaaaaaaaaaa (*Slap*) Ow!

GRINDLE Janice, how dare you hit your head hampster when he's got his eyes shut?

JANICE It's a radio play, Miss. You can do anything in radio plays.

ANGELA (*Nearer bell of a fire engine.*) The fire engine's getting nearer and nearer, girls!

INS And I can hear it.

ANGELA The fire engine must be coming to rescue the tiger from the flood. But the tiger is going mad because of the flood. It's biting every grown up in sight.

CYNTHIA Grrrrrr.

HEAD Owwwwwwwwww.

INS Well acted, head hampster. Ow. I almost felt its teeth myself. Oweeee.

GRINDLE Oweeeeeeeeeeeee.

DEIDRE Don't stop, Cynthia!

CYNTHIA I am, you don't know where they've been.

ROSE And look at the water rising down there. You'd better climb up on the windowledge with us now, tiger.

MARY The water's at Miss Grindle's tummy.

INS Pretend away, girls. By your dreams we shall know you!

GRINDLE The water's up to my tummy, and a bit more, head hampster. Shouldn't we—

ANGELA The baby and the blood can do nothing. They must just let the floods rise round them.

INS Of course they must. You've still got your eyes shut like me, haven't you, head hampster?

HEAD I have, sir. I can feel the water lapping inside my

shirt now, sir.

MARY Here girls, switch on that radio there on top of the cupboard. Let's see if there's any news of us being flooded.

ROSE Oh yes. It might be one of those rude plays again. (*Radio switched on. Tuning noises.*)

SHE Darling!

HE Darling!

SHE This sausage looks too good to eat!

HE And so do you darling!

SHE Do I darling?

HE Yes darling!

SHE Darling!

HE Darling!

(*Radio being retuned.*)

GIRLS (*except for Deirdre*) Oh Deirdre!

DEIRDRE That must be Radio Three. Let's try another station.

JANICE There's a snake up here on the cupboard as well.

GLYNIS And the tiger's opening the window to be rescued by the firemen who are ringing their bell down in the playground and sticking their ladders up to the window.

INS I can hear that as well. What poetry!

ANNOUNCER Here is an announcement. British Rail wish to apologise for the delays to trains today owing to a fl—

(*Radio being retuned.*)

DJ Kidsandkiddykinsandcatkins.NoyesIsaywellno-isnthatjustfabandgearandhere'sarequest,brills-villestyesit'srequesttime!

ROSE I've got a request. Shut up.

(*Radio being retuned. Near bell of a fire engine.*)

INS It's too, too, amazing. All except for the baby.

HEAD Baaaaaaa goooooooo babababababababa. How's that sir?

GRINDLE Head hampster, look, the water's up to my double chin now and—

HEAD Baaaaaaaaaaaaaaaaaaaaaaaaaaaaaaaaaaaaaaaa.

Ba Ba.

GRINDLE And it's still rising! The girls are safe because they're all up on top of the cupboards. But *we* shall drown.

INS Stop trying to spoil the play, Miss Tingly!

HEAD Agreed. Gaaaaaaaaaa. Glaaaa. Blub.

(*Near bell of a fire engine.*)

GIRLS Here we are. Help, help, help.

DEIRDRE Oh good idea, girls. We can pretend to call for pretend help from those pretend firemen running up their ladders to pretend to save us from the pretend flood.

INS More baby noises, head hampster. I'm sure a baby would be frightened by floods and fire engines. Glub. And some more rain I think, girls?

JANICE Crackers. Ssssssss!

CYNTHIA The tiger's going a bit barmy now. Grrrr.

HEAD Baaaaaaaaaaa ba baaaaaba glub glub.

INS And you, Miss Thingummy, are you imagining anything?

GRINDLE Glub Glub Glub.

INS At last. Now that *did* sound like blood.

GRINDLE It wasn't blood. It's me going down for the third t—Glub.

INS At last she's showing some imagination. She might not have to be sacked after all, head hampster?

HEAD You promised, sir.

GIRLS Help! Firemen, here we are on the windowledge.

DEIRDRE But there's no one here except us.

FIREMEN No need to fear
The firemen are here.

GIRLS Hurrah.

INS I can hear the firemen coming up their ladders. Eyes firmly shut, head hampstblub blub.

FIREMEN We never tire
Of fighting fire
It's our wondrous trade
Not to be afraid.

All is well
When you hear our bell.
(*Bell.*)

INS I can hear it, I can hear it.

CYNTHIA It's not a fire. It's a flood this time.

GLYNIS Their ladders won't reach!

DEIRDRE But they're putting out a big blanket for us all!

INS Such imaginations, glub, I could almost imagine I was drowning, myself.

FIREMEN Don't get in the dumps
You just have to jump
And you don't have time
For proper rhymes.

GIRLS We'll jump. Here we go girls.
(*Screaming of jumping girls. Bell ringing in triumph.*)

GIRLS (*Below and outside*) We're saved. Hurrah.

FIREMEN You've had your fun
The rescue's done
We've all done well
Let's ring the bell.
(*The bell rung in triumph. Pause.*)

INS That was very good, head hampster.
(*Clapping. Some of it under water.*)

HEAD Very good. I'll applaud too!
(*Clapping.*)

INS I'm going to open my glub eyes now, head hampster, and come out of the world of make believe... Oh, head hampster!

HEAD Certainly, sir. Babababababababababababababababababababababababababa!

INS Fool. The school's flooded, the girls have gone, we're drowning!

HEAD Right, sir, I think the baby would be more afraid than ever and after this play is over, sir, perhaps we could discuss my promotion to a better part of town.

INS And your teacher, Miss Dangle, is drowned. Open your eyes, fool!

HEAD Yes, do as you're told Miss Dangle.

INS *You*, head hampster.

HEAD Oh yes, sir. I am a fool, you're right. I'll open my eyes and...oh. It was *real*!

INS Put her on the top of that cupboard out of the water.

HEAD But sir—

INS And give her the kiss of life.

HEAD Anything but that!

INS Or else.

HEAD In. Out. In. Out.

INS And I'll meanwhile use the radio here to try to get us rescued.

(*Radio switched on.*)

HE Darling!

SHE Darling!

HE Darling!

(*Radio retuning.*)

ANNOUNCER Hello and good afternoon.

INS Hello. Listen. We're stranded in the top floor of the school and the water's rising all the time and the firemen have rescued the girls and gone home but we're still glub here and—

ANNOUNCER Well that's the end of the educational play for today. We hope you enjoyed it.

INS As a matter of fact we didn't but—

ANNOUNCER Charming!

INS I mean we didn't *listen*, listen!

ANNOUNCER You listen, I talk. That's what radio is all about.

INS We're drowning. You must get help.

ANNOUNCER I can't, the educational play is over.

HEAD In out in out in out uaghh.

GRINDLE Glub glub glub uagh.

INS Please help glub.

ANNOUNCER All that remains to be said is—make sure you switch all your taps off before going on to the next lesson. Goodbye children—everywhere.

RONY ROBINSON

Some questions to the playwright

Q Where did you get the idea?
A Out in our garden one sunny April Tuesday morning sitting in a deckchair with an exercise book and a 2B pencil.
Q And the idea came just like that?
A No. And if anyone knows how to get ideas to come just like that, write to me at once and we'll be rich and famous.
Q How did this particular idea come?
A Well...I sat in the garden. I hadn't got an idea. But I did know that on Wednesday morning a dozen schoolteachers would be meeting at the local radio station to record the play I hadn't written yet. Without that 'deadline' I would have read the paper, gone for a walk, cleaned my shoes, sharpened the pencil, put on some suncream, shaved... Anything's more fun than sitting down and writing.
Q I thought you were a writer?
A Who ever said it was supposed to be fun?
Q ?
A It's fun when you've done it. But starting off, each time, all over again, and realising how bad what you're writing is, and how someone's always already done it better...? That's not fun. Sometimes it stops you getting started at all—sometimes for years.
Q But you had the deadline so you started?
A I wrote the title and the first sound effect.
Q How long did it take to write?
A All morning, in pencil. about forty pages. And that's my only tip about writing—scribble it all down as fast as possible however daft it is, and however much you don't enjoy it. At least you'll have something to cross out after. Picasso the painter talked about how 'the canvas talks back'. I think I read that somewhere.
Q The 'canvas talking back'?

A Your own work tells you what to do next.
Q And did it?
A I spent the afternoon crossing most of it out, in biro. Then a couple of hours in the evening, sipping beer, trying to get my typewriter to spell it out in 12 pages.
Q It's supposed to be a funny play. Did you laugh as you wrote it?
A No.
Q Did it make you laugh afterwards?
A No. Funny eh?
Q What did the teachers think when they made their recording?
A Oh, they were too busy trying to read it properly. The local Chamber of Trade didn't like it, though.
Q Who were they?
A Mainly shopkeepers. They complained to the local newspaper that it was a 'sewer play' and their rates shouldn't be spent on sewer plays.
Q Why did they say that?
A There were six plays in the series and the shopkeepers said that they were not only a bit rude, (the plays not the shopkeepers, though I expect they were when the shops were shut)—but were, even worse, disrespectful of everyone in authority, like head hampsters and caretakers and policemen and school inspectors and vicars and shopkeepers and—adults in general really. And children in schools shouldn't be set such bad examples. Some kids, and some grown ups who'd listened as well, replied to the newspaper and said they didn't agree. A teacher wrote in saying it was only like the Bash Street Kids in the Beano. And someone else said it was only like Spike Milligan. And Joe Orton.
Q What did you think about that?
A I was dead chuffed. 'Only' like the Bash Street Kids! The plays never got broadcast again, mind you.
Q How did you choose the names of the characters?
A Well, Miss 'Grindle' just came when I was scribbling in pencil as fast I could. 'Grindle' sounds hard—and where I come from it's the name for a barren black rock. And you get 'grindle cakes' too but I don't know what they are. I called the caretaker 'Mr O'Shea' because my best pal's called O'Shea.
Q Is he a caretaker?
A No. But I'd once had another caretaker in a novel I wrote called *The Ted Carp Tradition* which is all about a revolution in a comprehensive school. I bet they've not got that in your school library! Oh and 'McChoakumchild' is pinched from Charles Dickens—he always had fun with names. Your teacher'll know which book if you ask.

Q It's supposed to be a funny play—did you write it just to make people laugh?
A What do you mean 'just'?
Q Has it got a message?
A Some writer once said—your teacher'll know—that if writers wanted to send messages, they should write telegrams, or something like that.
Q Has it got a message?
A What do you mean by 'message'?
Q Do you want anything to change because people have read your play or acted it or listened to it?
A Ah. Well. Something does change when you read or act or listen to plays together, doesn't it?
Q Like what?
A Like, it's not a bad way of passing a bit of time at school for a start. And making plays together is a very civilised thing to do—all the co-operating, that's involved. A theatre director I know talks about how 'optimistic' making theatre is—everybody, including the audience, comes together in one place at one time to share and pretend things together...But I'd better be careful. That's the kind of stuff the Inspector talks in the play, and look where he ended up...Ask me if I've any tips about performing the play.
Q Have you any tips about performing the play?
A Do what you want with it, make it yours. But it has to go fast—'like manure off a shovel', as we (nearly) say in the theatre. That doesn't mean speaking fast—but it does mean picking up your 'cues' fast—coming in with your speech or effect immediately on the end of the previous one, if not earlier.
Q What happened to the Naughty Girls after?
A The sequel?
Q Yes, '*How Mavis Met Gary Blood*'.
A There was another sunny morning, and another deadline and who knows, one day there may be a further play, but I think it will be called 'What Happened When Deirdre fell in Love With The Man From The Chamber of Trade'...But you can write *that* sequel yourself if you get any better ideas!

RONY ROBINSON

How Mavis Met Gary Blood

CHARACTERS

HEADMASTER
MISS GRINDLE
CYNTHIA
JANICE
MARY
ROSE
MAVIS
DEIRDRE
ANGELA
ARTHUR FLOP
MOTHER
EDITOR
MR BIG
MISS BROWN
LARRY
BARRY
PC
UNDERPAID WOMAN
GARY BLOOD
FATHER
RADIO INTERVIEWER
EXPERT

1 *The Headmaster's Study*

HEAD Come in. Oh, it's only you Miss Grindle. Well?

GRINDLE Quite well thank you headmaster.

HEAD I mean, Grindle, 'Well what is it?'

GRINDLE I don't know headmaster. You sent for me.

HEAD I must be mad...Yes, it's about your girls. Your girls are getting very naughty.

GRINDLE I'm sure I try my best headmaster.

HEAD Your best is no good, Grindle. Your girls are like wild animals. Listen.

(*The distant noise of wild animals.*)

HEAD We are getting an inspector at the school next week. Pull up your socks, Grindle. Or you will get the boot. And then you will not have a leg to stand on.

GRINDLE That's not very *knees*, headmaster.

HEAD What's that?

GRINDLE A joke, headmaster.

HEAD Have you gone completely mad? *I* make the jokes in this school. Get back to your girls. Have some interesting discussions. Be firm but kind, like me. Go!

(*Whistle.*)

GRINDLE Thank you, headmaster. Three bags full, headmaster.

2 *The Corridor*

(*Miss Grindle's feet walking.*)

GRINDLE I'll show those girls. I will do the most interesting discussion lesson there has ever been. I'll be kind but firm. Or was it firm but kind? (*The nearer noise of wild animals.*)

GRINDLE Girls? Open this door. Please. Girls?

(*Knocking at door.*)

JANICE Welcome to the zoo, Miss Grindle.

CYNTHIA Have you come to watch through the window or are you in it, Miss Grindle?

GRINDLE Please open this door and let me in.
MARY Quick girls, it's the keeper.
ROSE Back in your cages, girls.

3 *The Classroom*

(*Door opening.*)
GRINDLE That's better. Now—
(*Wild animals, near.*)
GRINDLE Will you stop that? And stop talking. How can we have a discussion lesson if you keep talking? Right, today we are going to have the best discussion lesson anyone has ever had. And the next person to speak will come out here and speak.
MAVIS Charming.
GRINDLE And you are the next person to speak, Mavis. Come out here. Stand up straight. Pull that in. Breathe deeply and we're off.
JANICE She's off all right.
GLYNIS She's crackers.
DEIRDRE What hope have we got with teachers like her.
GRINDLE Stop talking you lot. And start talking you, Mavis.
MAVIS What about, Miss?
GRINDLE Whatever interests you. We talk best when we talk about what we're interested in.
DEIRDRE Let me have a go, Miss Grindle. You know what I'm interested in.
GRINDLE We all know, Deirdre. You just keep taking the tablets.
MAVIS Charming.
GRINDLE Good, Mavis. You have started. Now what are you interested in?
MAVIS Gary Blood.
GRINDLE Oh and what's that, Mavis? A biscuit?
MAVIS Gary Blood, Miss. I met him.
ANGELA Listen to Mavis, girls!
GLYNIS She's talking!

ROSE Oh yes, girls. I shall remember this moment for the rest of my life.

MARY It's like that kid in that film who had that eagle that got murdered.

GRINDLE Girls. Shshshsh. Tell me what your talk's called, Mavis, and I'll write it on the board. (Aside) This is the way to teach. Be kind but firm. Or is it firm but kind?

CYNTHIA She's talking to herself again.

MARY First signs.

MAVIS It's called 'How Mavis Met Gary Blood And What She Said To Him'.

GRINDLE Charming.

MAVIS Don't start spoiling it or I'll stop.

GIRLS Don't spoil it, Miss.

MAVIS It all began with Socko's Sausages.

GRINDLE Good. I'll write sausages on the board.

GIRLS Stop starting spoiling it, Miss.

MAVIS We eat a lot of Socko Sausages at our house. And what happened was that my dad started to turn purple and all his hair fell out. So my mum got out the Yellow Pages, and rang up the sausage people.

4 *Mavis's House*

(Telephone ringing tone. The phone at the other end lifted.)

MOTHER Hello? Hello?

ARTHUR (*at the other end of the phone*) Socko. Socko. Socko. Socko! The sausage that sings.

MOTHER Here, is that Socko? Because my Wally's going purple and his hair's fallen out. It's something in your sausages. You've damaged him. And I want some damages from you.

ARTHUR Thanks for calling, caller. Glad you enjoyed the sausages. This is a recording so it's no use ringing us to complain. There's nobody here. I'm just a voice on a tape. I'm in South America at the moment in fact. Bye. Socko. Socko. Socko. The sausage that sucks. (*Click and dialling tone.*)

MOTHER Well. I don't know. Honestly. I mean to say. I'm going to tell the newspapers I am. Yellow pages again. Thank goodness we did alphabetical order when I was a schoolgirl. Kids nowadays don't learn a thing at school. Especially our Mavis and that loony Miss Grindle. Now then. Stab, Stackable, Staff, Stanley, Staples, Stair newspaper. This is it. 364635.

(*Dialling, ringing tone. The phone at the other end lifted.*)

EDITOR (*at the other end of the phone.*) This is the Odd-eater of the Syair spiking.

MOTHER Right. I've got a story.

EDITOR Whit?

MOTHER I've got news for you.

EDITOR Nudes? For page free?

MOTHER Listen. I'm a mother and my husband has had his health damaged by some sausages and I'm going to tell all.

EDITOR Till thin! Till thin.

MOTHER Ask Socko why my Wally has gone purple and bald.

EDITOR I wool. Thinks for the tap. I'll get straight on to the sausage pope.

(*Telephone replaced and dialling tone.*)

MOTHER I mean to say. Well did you ever. I don't know what things are coming to. Newspapers that can't even spell right when they're talking.

5 *Socko Sausages. Downstairs*

(*Telephone ringing. Lifted up.*)

ARTHUR Socko socko socko socko. The sausage that shines.

EDITOR (*at the other end of the line*) The editor of the Star here. Trouble. We've got a tip-off about the dangerous sausages again.

ARTHUR What is it this time?

EDITOR *MASS CITY SICKNESS IN SAUSAGE SCANDAL.* Then under that *HAIR LOSS FEAR FLARE UP* and *CITY MAN HUE CHANGE SHOCK.*

ARTHUR Oh deary deary deary. I'll tell Mr Big and come back to you with a statement from our spokesman.

EDITOR But you don't need to—

ARTHUR No comment till then.

(*Phone crashed down.*)

ARTHUR I'll run upstairs to the penthouse suite and report this in person to Mr Big. I may even get promotion for this.

6 *The Stairs at Socko Sausages*

(*A man running up many stairs.*)

ARTHUR (breathless) Socko. Socko. Socko. Sooooock-ooooooo.

7 *Mr Big's Office*

(*Timid knock.*)

MR BIG In.

ARTHUR (*very breathless*) I've c–

MR BIG On your knees.

ARTHUR Sorry Mr Big. Sir, it's the newspapers sir. Our sausages sir. They say they're dangerous sir. People are losing their hair and changing colour sir.

MR BIG Is that all?

(*Buzzer.*)

MISS B Yes, Mr Big sir?

MR BIG Send in my public relations men Larry and Barry, Miss Brown.

MISS B Yes, Mr Big.

MR BIG And you're not kneeling, Miss Brown.

MISS B I am now sir. I didn't know you would be buzzing me, Mr Big, sir.

MR BIG Out!

(*Buzzer.*)

MR BIG Now then you, whatever your name is.

ARTHUR Arthur Flop, sir.

MR BIG I don't want to know what your name is. You've no name. I own Socko Sausages. You do the work. I get the money. You go home. Right?

ARTHUR Yes sir but–

MR BIG I don't only own Socko either. I own steelworks and breweries and shops and lots and lots of houses and land. And I also tend to own newspapers. You won't know that because I use many different names. I'm sometimes the Duke of This or the Lord of That or the Sir of the Other. But it's all me. I get up every day rich, do not work, and go to bed at night richer. If you don't like it, start your own business. Meanwhile–

(*Two men knocking at a door.*)

MR BIG In!

BARRY Hello, Mr B.

LARRY Hello, Mr B.

BARRY I hope your carpet's clean. These are my new velvet jeans.

LARRY I think they're mine actually. Still, down we go.

MR BIG Boys! Boys! Socko Sausages.

LARRY Socko. Socko. Socko. Socko.

BARRY Socko. Socko. Socko. Socko.

MR BIG I've had a complaint, boys.

BARRY We had that, Mr B.

LARRY The hospital was very good, Mr B.

MR BIG A complaint about Socko Sausages.

LARRY No, Mr B!

MR BIG People's hair is falling out and they're going purple.

LARRY We know all about that, Mr B.

BARRY That's why we put the message on the skins, Mr B.

LARRY 'Government Health Warning. Socko Sausages Can Damage Your Health'.

ARTHUR Is that true then, Mr Big? Has the government

been brought in?

MR BIG Who is this fool, boys?

ARTHUR I'm Arthur Flop, sir, and–

MR BIG I don't want to know who you are. I want you to know who I am. I am, under other names, also the government. Now then boys, there is a danger that some militants will make trouble for us by trying to stop us producing Socko Sausages. That would throw many people out of work. So I want you two public relations boys to think up a brilliant plan so Socko's sell even more sausages. Ideas, ideas.

(*Finger clicking.*)

LARRY How about Finger Clicking Good?

BARRY We could put stripes in the sausages, like sticks of rock, Mr B?

MR BIG Good idea, Larry.

LARRY We could say we'll give extra value with every sausage, Mr B?

MR BIG Bad idea, Barry.

LARRY But in fact what we do is make the wrappers bigger and heavier, the sausages smaller and the price higher, Mr B?

MR BIG Better idea now, Barry. And what do you want, little man on the floor with your hand up? Time's money you know. Your time, my money.

ARTHUR If the sausages *are* poisoning people, sir, shouldn't we stop selling them?

BARRY Shhhhhhhh.

MR BIG We have thousands and thousands of them in the warehouses. And thousands more are made every day. Do you want to wreck the economy? They are all waiting ready to be gobbled up by the hungry workers who stagger home after a hard day's work in my factories. How would they be able to afford them if my sausages were no longer being made? Where would their wages come from? As it is, they come home, they eat my sausages.

BARRY Then chew your indigestion pills, Mr B.

LARRY Then smoke your cigarettes, Mr B.

BARRY Then watch your television programmes, Mr B.

LARRY And then go to bed on your beds, Mr B.

BARRY So they are bright and early in the morning to go off to your factories, Mr B.

LARRY To earn their wages so it can all start again, Mr B.

MR BIG Right. Right. Now give me some ideas boys to calm me down. How do we get people to eat more sausages and provide more jobs?

BARRY Let's offer a prize to someone for winning a competition organised by Socko Sausages, the sausages that smile.

LARRY If we make it daft enough nobody will enter for it.

BARRY But you can still claim tax relief on it.

MR BIG I like it. I like it. If you can think of something really cheap?

LARRY Er.

BARRY Er, er.

LARRY Got it.

BARRY He has, Mr B.

LARRY Gary Blood, Mr B.

MR BIG What is it, a biscuit?

BARRY He's a pop singer, Mr B.

MR BIG That's all right. I own most of them. The Beatens. Elvis Puzzle. The Rolling Pins. Johnny Clash. And their records. And the record players for playing the records. The Jamjars. Shirley Busman. Adman and the Nits. Go on boys, keep being creative.

BARRY Er.

LARRY Er, er.

BARRY Got it!

MR BIG Give, boys, give.

LARRY People have to make up a slogan, Mr B.

BARRY And the prize is to meet Gary Blood, Mr B.

LARRY We tell them to fill in a word on a slogan to say how good Socko Sausages are.

ARTHUR But they're poisoning people sir.

MR BIG One more word from you whosoever you are—

ARTHUR Arthur Flop sir and—

LARRY Got it.

BARRY We've both got it.

LARRY I like eating Socko Sausages because they're—

MR BIG Because they're what?

LARRY That's it, Mr B.

BARRY That's what they fill in. Like, 'I like eating Socko Sausages because they're—nice'.

LARRY Lovely.

BARRY Squelchy.

LARRY Squadgy.

BARRY Skinny.

ARTHUR Poisonous.

MR BIG That's it. You're fired.

(Gunshot and man dying in pain.)

(Buzzer.)

MR BIG Miss Brown.

MISS B I'm on my knees, Mr Big.

MR BIG Come in when we have finished and collect the body of an unemployed workman. Then ring up his widow reversing the charges and advise her that Mr Big Funerals do a lively service. If she wants to sue us tell her to try Big Big Big and Big, Solicitors.

MISS B At once, Mr Big. And Mr Big, there's a policeman on the phone for you. Something about sausages.

MR BIG I've got this game of golf with the Freemasons. Put him through Miss Brown. And take a cut in salary for making a ba-ba.

MISS B Yes, Mr Big. I have Mr Big for you now.

MR BIG What?

PC I have a tip off about persons being poisoned by your sausages, sir.

MR BIG Who are you, Constable?

PC PC Shirt sir, proceeding with my duties.

MR BIG Perhaps I should tell you that I am a good friend of the chief constable.

PC It's nice to have friends sir. Now then this poison case—

MR BIG I'm also Chairman of the Watch Committee. I think you should watch it.

PC Thanks for the advice sir. Now about these poisonous sausages, sir—

MR BIG And tell your sergeant I shall be sending my usual huge cheque for the police ball.

PC Thank you, sir. Now, as to the sausages—

MR BIG I think it might be easier if I made the cheque out to you, PC Shirt, to a numbered bank account.

PC Are you trying to bribe a police officer in the course of his duty, sir?

MR BIG I am.

PC Very well, sir. And I am happy to tell you that I have investigated the tip-off about the sausages and am glad to say there is no evidence and we shall take action against the person who complained for making a malicious complaint. Goodbye sir and thank you for your assistance in clearing this matter up.

(*Telephone click and dialling tone.*)

MR BIG Right, boys. Ideas.

BARRY We print some leaflets and get them delivered.

LARRY By those women who push all that rubbish through the letter boxes with tokens for 5p off things you don't want.

MR BIG Good idea, Barry.

BARRY And we'll put in some of that drug so that once you start eating them you can't stop.

MR BIG Good idea, Larry. I'm off to play golf with The Great Wizard from the Freemasons. Pick up my golf clubs and follow me on your knees to my tax deductible Rolls Royce.

BARRY Yes, Mr B.

LARRY Yes, Mr B.

8 *The Classroom*

MAVIS What do you think of it so far, Miss Grindle?

GRINDLE I think you should open your mouth a little more, Mavis, and I did not like that bit when your mother made a certain remark about a teacher who—

GIRLS Stop carrying on trying to spoil it, Miss.

MAVIS Anyway, what happened was, I was sitting in our house looking at Blue Peter waiting for Gary Blood to come on and launch a lifeboat, and watching them make a life-size model of Scotland Yard with Yoghurt cartons and I heard a scream.

9 *Mavis's House*

WOMAN Aaaaaaaaaagahahahahahahahaaahahahahahaa.

MAVIS Charming.

WOMAN Aaaaahahaha.

MAVIS What's up then? And don't say the sky.

WOMAN Aagaaah. I'm outside your front door trying to post you these leaflets about the new Socko campaign but you're the first house I've come to and I've trapped my fingers in your letter box.

MAVIS It's that strong spring my dad put on to stop burglars. I'll lift the lid.

WOMAN Tahangaahahahahahahahahanks.

MAVIS Take your fingers out when I lift then. Ready. Go.

WOMAN Aagaaaaaaa.

MAVIS Now go away.

WOMAN (*getting further and further away*) Agahahah.

MAVIS Now then, what's this rubbish she's left? 'A Socko Promotion'. Hello, this is a picture of Gary Blood eating a sausage. And what's it say in this balloon here coming out of his mouth?

GARY Hello girls. Would you like to meet me at the City Hall and say something to me?

MAVIS Oh yes please.

GARY Well you can. All you need to do is fill in one

word on the slogan below, enclose ten Socko sausage skins and Bobs Your Auntie. Bye, for now.

MAVIS Bye, Gary, for now. Let me see. 'I eat Socko Sausages because they're dot dot dot.' I know what to put. C.H.A.R.M.I.N.G. And I'll fold this up now, get some sausage skins from the fridge and send off for Gary.

FATHER (*inside cupboard*) Mavis, here, our Mavis?

MAVIS Dad! What are you doing in that cupboard?

FATHER I'm too ashamed to go out now, Mavis. I've gone even more purple and I've no hairs anywhere. I'm starving and mum is too busy all the time trying to get publicity for my tragedy to get me any food. Get me a sausage to be going on with will you?

MAVIS I haven't time, dad. I've got to post my letter to Gary. But I'll switch on the local radio for you to take your mind off it. Bye, dad.

RADIO And we've another caller on the line. And what's your question to our panel of experts, caller?

MOTHER Our Wally's losing his hairs all over the carpet and—

RADIO Thank you, caller. A problem with Wally's hairs, panel of experts?

EXPERT There is nothing to worry about, caller. Moulting is quiet common at this time of the year. Is he changing colour at all?

MOTHER Yes.

EXPERT Good. That's perfectly normal. Try him with worm powder and put him out at night in the garden. Next caller?

MOTHER Are you mad? My Wally's not a dog. He was my husband 'till he turned purple because of the Socko Sausag—

(*Bleeping.*)

RADIO I'm sorry listeners, we seem to have lost that caller. Let's have the next pet question please?

10 *The Classroom*

MAVIS Are you following, Miss?

GRINDLE Yes I am, Mavis, and I am afraid you might be tempted to make it a little coarse.

GIRLS Stop spoiling it yet again, Miss.

MAVIS This is what happened. I ripped the skins off the last ten sausages that were lurking there in the fridge because my dad couldn't get at them because he was locked in his cupboard. I put them with the form. Then I went to the post box. Then I posted them. Then I came home.

GRINDLE No, no, Mavis. You're getting tired. You have to describe things, paint pictures with language. It's no use going 'then' and then 'then'. Use words.

DEIRDRE What do you think she's using now, fresh air?

MAVIS It was a bright spring morning a few weeks later, and the whole of our estate smelt of magnolia and dogs. I received no gentle valentine from my Gary. And I did not know what was happening at Socko's either. But what was happening was this...

11 *Socko Sausages*

(*Two men knocking at a door.*)

MR BIG In. Don't kneel. Explain and prepare to join the dole queue.

BARRY It's that sausage competition, Mr B.

LARRY The one about Gary Blood.

BARRY We got an entry, Mr B.

LARRY And it included ten sausage skins as required, Mr B.

BARRY And a slogan.

LARRY It's come from a smelly girl called Mavis.

BARRY So it's smelly Mavis who will have to meet Gary Blood.

LARRY Only we don't want to have to pay Gary Blood

any money.

MR BIG You've got yourselves in a bit of tizz boys. Ideas, ideas.

LARRY Er.

BARRY Er, er, er.

LARRY I dress up as Gary, Mr B.

BARRY And when he comes on stage at the City Hall I switch out the lights, Mr B.

LARRY And this smelly girl says 'hello' just as we cancel the concert because the lights have fused. And that's it.

MR BIG Good idea, Barry. What other new ideas for making me even more money?

BARRY We're getting the underpaid workmen to put that drug in the strips of the sausage, so once you've had one you crave for another and then another, until you die.

MR BIG Good idea, Larry. Next?

LARRY We're making up a new radio commercial with a love interest for the radio.

BARRY We've got the love interest, Mr B.

LARRY We just can't fit in the sausages, Mr B.

BARRY It starts like this.

LARRY Darling!

BARRY Darling!

LARRY Darling!

BARRY Darling!

MR BIG Fine, boys, fine. Let me hear it as soon as you fit the sausage angle.

12 *Classroom*

GRINDLE Then what, Mavis?

MAVIS I got a letter inviting me to go and see Gary, 'course.

GRINDLE There's no 'course' about it. Make the most of your tale, Mavis. Tell us in the language of Shakespeare. Use words. We don't know what happened even if you do.

JANICE We do, Miss.

GLYNIS We went with Mavis, see, Miss.

ANGELA So you needn't have got Mavis talking, Miss. We know it already.

DEIRDRE It's all been for you, all this, Miss.

MAVIS We went to the City Hall.

MARY There was no one there but us.

ROSE It was a secret concert for Mavis.

CYNTHIA As a reward for her sausage skins.

DEIRDRE And then it happened.

GLYNIS *It* did, Miss.

DEIRDRE Well they don't call us weenyboppers for nothing.

MARY We weenied.

ANGELA And we bopped.

DEIRDRE All over the place.

MAVIS Don't spoil it, girls.

GRINDLE No don't spoil it, girls.

MAVIS I got there and there was an announcement over the announcement thing.

LARRY (*disguised*) For your delight weenyboppers everywhere—he's played in front of the Prince of Wales. He's played in front of the Queen. And he's played in front of a lot of other pubs too and here he is—Gary Blood.

(*Screaming of girls or wild animals.*)

MAVIS And then the lights went out.

GIRLS Aaaaaaaaaaah.

MAVIS I struggled to the stage. I lit a match just under Gary's smiling face. And I spoke to him. I said...

GIRLS Charming.

GRINDLE Charming.

MAVIS Don't spoil it, it's nearly over.

DEIRDRE You see it wasn't Gary was it, Mavis?

JANICE It was Larry disguised as Gary.

MAVIS So I rushed into the foyer and bought a Socko Sausage Hot Dog and I ran back in, and I stuck the sausage up Gary's nose, only it wasn't Gary, and then the bread, and as many of the onions as I could force up.

DEIRDRE And we other girls did the same, didn't we girls?

GIRLS Yes, Deirdre.

DEIRDRE Out with the sausage.

GIRLS And up with the sausage.

MAVIS And then his hair fell out and he went purple. And then I went home. And that's the end. (*End of lesson signal.*)

GRINDLE Dash. No, Deirdre stay where you are. I don't mean *dash* dash, I mean dash, oh what a pity. I wanted the headmaster to come and see my interesting discussion lesson as a result of my being firm and kind...or kind and firm...or fur and mind. Will you stay behind now and practise, Mavis, so we can have the discussion lesson again next week when the Inspector comes? And you other girls I'm sure wouldn't mind staying on for a few minutes to...oh, they've all gone. I can see them there through the window, round Mavis, thanking her for her lovely talk.

13 *The Playground*

DEIRDRE Did you just make it up on the spur of the moment, Mavis?

MAVIS Yes.

ROSE Just as it came out of your head?

MAVIS Yes.

CYNTHIA And it just kept on coming, all that about sausages and advertising, and your mum and dad and all that?

MAVIS Yes, did you like it?

GIRLS No, Mavis. It was rubbish.

MAVIS Charming

DEIRDRE And that's another thing we girls have decided. We're going to smack you every time you say 'Charming' from now on because it's starting to get on our nerves, isn't it girls?

GIRLS Yes, Deirdre, it is Mavis.

MAVIS Charming!

DEIRDRE That's it.

MAVIS No girls, please girls, don't. I did stop us having to do any writing all last lesson. Please...

(Lots of slapping.)

GRINDLE *(from the classroom window)* Charming, charming.

HELEN CRESSWELL

For Bethlehem, Read Little Thraves

CHARACTERS

MAGGIE
SARAH *schoolgirls*
WENDY
BEN *a shepherd*
DORA *Maggie's mother*
TED *Maggie's father*
KATE *a new girl*
MRS ROBINSON *Kate's mother*
MRS GARTON *the teacher*
FIRST CHILD
SECOND CHILD
THIRD CHILD
HEROD *actors in the school*
SHEPHERD *Nativity play*
CONGREGATION

1 *Day. Village*

(Music. Shot of small village of grey stone houses set in rolling country with dry stone walls. Sheep in fields.
Mix to shot of outskirts of village and signpost 'Little Thraves'. In distance we see backs of three

girls all with long dark hair.
Camera tracks them closer but still behind, 'eaves-dropping' as it were. They are on their way home from school.
Sheep bleating faintly in distance.)

SARAH She's going to decide tomorrow. She said so. It'll be between us three.

WENDY You can't have a Mary wi' fair hair. Look *daft*, that would...

MAGGIE Or ginger. Betty Dobbs'll never be Mary, not as long as she lives. Got *freckles* as well.

SARAH But even if it's dark, got to be *long*...

WENDY All the fair hairs'll be angels, or summat.

SARAH Between us three, anyhow. (*Tosses her hair*) Mine's *longest*...

MAGGIE (*passionately*) But you were it last year! And you ain't been growing your hair special. Only to me ears m' hair was in't summer. *'Tis* long enough for Mary, I know it is!

WENDY (*not feeling so strongly*) Well, I ain't been it, neither. Come on, Sarah...see you tomorrow.
(*Wendy and Sarah branch off along side lane.*)

MAGGIE 'Bye. 'Bye, Sarah.
(*Maggie walks on alone. Camera follows Wendy & Sarah.*)

SARAH She ain't pretty enough. Not for Mary. 'T'ain't *just* dark hair...
(*She gives head another smug toss.*)

2 Day. Village shop-cum-post office

(*Maggie just approaching small post office-cum-village shop.*)

MAGGIE (*thinks*) Is't still there? Oooh, let it be!
(*Shot of shop window and zoom in to rather small, cheap looking doll's house among other toys.*
Shop door opens. A woman in advanced state of pregnancy comes out. Her hair is lank, her face depressed and her clothes poor. A small, thin girl of

about six, also pale and ill-kempt, is clinging to her hand.
Shot of Maggie staring at them curiously.
Maggie follows them, walking behind, and sees them enter shabby little cottage in row. Child looks back at Maggie before door shuts.)

3 *Day. Small farmyard*

(*Maggie entering small farmyard. She runs and looks into stable.*
Shot of baby donkey with its mother.)

MAGGIE Oooh, you little beauty! You get standing and walking proper, and *you'll* be in Nativity. *Was* a donkey, you know, in stable when Jesus was born. (*Speculatively*) *Still* don't know what to call you, though. Got to think o' *summat Christmassy, see...*

(*She turns away from stable. Old Shepherd is herding several fat ewes into disused pig styes. Floor is littered with straw. Maggie runs to join him.*)

MAGGIE Ben! They're 't' first, ain't they? When'll they lamb, Ben?

BEN (*not looking at her*)
Come they're ready. Not so far on.

MAGGIE (*eagerly*)
Afore Christmas, though? In time for't Nativity? Don't *seem* like Christmas without lambs.

BEN (*busying himself spreading straw*)
Aye. That all reet. Early this to bring 'em down. Let 'em loose in't home field in't morning. Snow, there'll be soon. Don't want 'em up there in snow.

MAGGIE (*delighted*)
Snow? Who says? Did't forecast?

(*Ben fastens pen door and after final look at sheep turns and goes across farmyard to cottage adjoining it. Maggie follows.*)

BEN *I* say. Not been shepherding these fells these

sixty odd year and not smell snow coming.

4 *Day. Ben's Cottage*

(*Ben enters and Maggie follows.*)

MAGGIE Snow *and* lambs! And Ben—it's tomorrow! Oooh, d'*you* think I'll be Mary?

(*Ben is all the time busying himself preparing a meal in the manner of a man who has always lived alone and fended for himself.*)

BEN Not be for want of trying, if th'ain't.

MAGGIE (*anxiously*)
But is my *hair* right?

BEN (*grunts*)
Hair's all reet. Right nice hair, when it's had a comb through it.

MAGGIE (*half to herself*)
Wash it tonight, I shall. Ben...?

BEN (*preoccupied, grunts.*)

MAGGIE Ben...d'you ever make *bargains*? You know—wi' yourself?

BEN (*still preoccupied*) What bargains them, then?

MAGGIE Well...like if f'r' instance...if...S'pose I wanted to go to't Panto in town. Right? And s'pose...S'pose I wanted a bike for Christmas—I know I don't, but if I *did*...Well, I could make a sort o' bargain wi' meself, for one or't' other. I could wish for't Panto, see, and sort of say, 'If only I can go to't Panto, I don't mind not getting bike. (*Pauses*) Or't'other way round, o'course.

(*Ben hardly ever looks at Maggie while* he *is speaking, but occasionally glances at her while* she *is —as now.*)

BEN Rum kind o' game to play that is. Can't reckon how *that'd* work.

MAGGIE (*nods confidently*) Oh, it can. Not always, mind, but it can. Done it afore.

(*Ben fills teapot and puts it on table and puts cosy on.*)

BEN You stopping, or your own tea to get?

MAGGIE Going. 'Bye, Ben.
(*Maggie exits.*)

5 *Farmyard*

(*Maggie walks only a few yards to door of own house also bordering farmyard.*)

MAGGIE Mam!
(*she goes in.*)

6 *Maggie's house, kitchen*

DORA (*entering kitchen*) There you are!

MAGGIE Ben says it'll snow! And there'll be lambs soon he says...

DORA (*not really listening*) Get your things off will you, Maggie, and give a hand wi't tea. Your father'll be back, and I'm not half done.
(*Maggie takes off coat and helps Dora with preparing tea.*)

MAGGIE There's new folk in't village. Saw 'em. There's a woman, and there's a girl—about six, I reckon. *And* there's another coming.

DORA Aye. Well. Old Dolly Barnes's place, were it?

MAGGIE (*nods*) Aye. Thought that wan't meant to be fit to live in, that house. What they said when she died.

DORA (*sourly*) Reckon it'll do reet enough for't likes of her.

MAGGIE (*looks up from buttering bread*) Her? The new one? D'you know her then, Mam?

DORA Know enough, thank you. Niece o' Dolly's, that she left't cottage to.

MAGGIE (*persisting*) But *why't* it good enough for her? What's she done?

DORA Oh leave off, will you, Maggie, and get that butter spread.
(*Maggie does so. Thinks for a moment then changes*

subject.)

MAGGIE (*with hope*) That doll's house is still there. (*No response.*) Smashing, it is. Never had a doll's house I ain't.

DORA (*unmoved*) And too big for one now. Whatever's a great lass like you want wi' doll's house? Tuppeny ha'penny bit of a thing!

MAGGIE (*hopeful again*) Oh—you've *seen* it, then?

DORA Aye. And I've seen price, an' all. Four pounds fifty! Nobbut plastic and cardboard!

(*Maggie lets out resigned sigh. Pause then changes subject again.*)

MAGGIE Will you wash me hair, Mam, after tea?

DORA (*surprised*) 'T'ain't Friday?

MAGGIE (*eagerly*) No, but it's *tomorrow*! Mrs Garton's choosing for't Nativity. And Mary—s'between us three. There's me, and Sarah Baisley and Wendy. And it's your hair, see, that's got to be right. *Please*, Mam...

DORA (*noncommital*) Well, we'll see...

(*Maggie with newly washed hair sitting on rug before fire gently tossing her hair. Gazes into flames.*)

MAGGIE (*talking into fire*) Oh...Mary...wi' a long blue dress and a big yeller halo...Ooo...which'd I rather? That—or't doll's house...? Don't think Mam'd get me that anyhow. Make a bargain then, I will...(*shuts eyes*) I'll not have doll's house. I wish not to get doll's house. Mary...I'll be Mary...oh, and the baby donkey an' all... (*opens eyes*)'Sdone,then...

7 *Living room*

(*Maggie has already had breakfast and is collecting things together for school. She enters carrying book as Dora and Ted sit at table.*)

TED (*looks up as Maggie enters*) Here's our Mary, then.

MAGGIE (*pleased nonetheless*) Oh *Dad*...not *definite.*

(*Thinks*) *Near* definite, all right...(*Aloud*) You'll come, shan't you, Dad—if I am, I mean?

TED On—reckon sheep'll look after theirsen an hour or two. Come and give you a clap.

DORA Not *clap*, Ted. You don't clap, not at Nativities. Like being in church.

(*Sound of letter box.*)

There's post. (*She goes out.*)

TED Aye. Well. Give you a wink, eh? Or ain't winking allowed, neither?

MAGGIE Shouldn't be able to wink back, Dad. Can't *wink*, not Mary...I should have a *halo* remember...

(*Dora re-enters shuffling through letters.*)

DORA One here for you, Maggie. From your Aunt Beryl, that'll be.

(*She hands letter to Maggie. Maggie tears it open. A five pound note falls out from inside Christmas Card. Maggie seizes it.*)

MAGGIE (*delighted*) Oooh! Look!

TED (*through mouthful of food*) Lend us a fiver, can you?

MAGGIE She on'y ever *sends* a pound...

DORA Aye. Well. Been sending a pound note these last eight years. Just about heard about 't inflation, I reckon. And like her to send it minute clocks change. Talk about post early. If she's a train to catch she's sat there waiting for it three hours before it's due.

(*End of this speech can be overlapped with Maggie's spoken thought.*)

MAGGIE (*half to herself*) Five pound...the doll's house...

(*Ted and Dora exchange glances.*)

TED (*clearing throat*) Well...shouldn't go rushing in, our Maggie. Plenty o' other things you could get, when you've had time to think. You'll not be getting many five pound notes for a bit.

MAGGIE But I've never had a doll's house.

DORA And too old for one *now.* I've told you—next year and you'll be out o' doll's houses, Maggie, and four pound fifty down't drain.

MAGGIE (*half defiant*) It's my money.

(*Ted and Dora again exchange glances.*)

TED Oh, that's all right. But you wait on, Maggie. Take your time, eh?

MAGGIE (*nods reluctantly*) Right, Dad.

(*She puts note back into envelope and puts it in her pocket.*)

DORA Best get off, Maggie. Half past eight now.

(*Maggie takes satchel from hook.*)

TED And let's have you come back Mary, shall we?

(*Maggie buttons her coat and looks at herself in mirror and tosses hair.*)

MAGGIE Hair's right enough, anyhow...'bye!

(*She goes out.*)

8 Ben's House

(*Ben is fetching something out of large cupboard. Ted goes over*)

TED Here, give you a hand.

(*They place on table a doll's house. It is very large and made of wood and already partly painted. Ben takes hold of knob and pulls and whole front of Doll's house swings open. They all stand and gaze at it.*)

TED Eh, well...got on a bit since I last see it, Ben.

DORA And her mithering after that tuppeny ha'penny bit of a thing in't Post Office!

TED Aye, but don't know about this, Dora, do she?

DORA Beautiful this is. Right beautiful, Ben. Don't get doll's houses like this in a shop, not for *twenty* pound, let alone four. Just look at them little stairs...and't fireplace looks that real you could light a fire in it—ooh, and look, Ted—little hob and poker and coal scuttle and all!

TED It'll be summat to see our Maggie's face when she sees this, right enough. Give Ben them bits o' things you've been making, Dora.

DORA Oh well—not much. Just out of a few scraps, and that. Chairs, see, and sofa...and a little light. Let's put 'em in and see how they look. (*She places items in living room.*) Right size are they, you reckon?

BEN Right nice they are, Dora. Make it look proper lived in, them do.

DORA And beds—here's beds. Ted made 'em, see, out o' wood, and I've made covers. And curtains, look, to match. (*She puts these in bedroom. She is pleased and half excited despite herself.*) Mmm. Do right enough, they will. (*She digs in carrier and brings out scraps of carpet.*) And try these, shall you, for carpets? Cut 'em to size, see, how you like. This one, I thought, for living room, to go wi' chairs and that... (*Fishes out piece of carpet of matching colour.*)

BEN Aye. Them's nice, Dora.

TED How about t'wallpaper? Get some bits, shall I?

BEN Get all lights in fust, then wallpaper. Same as you would yoursen.

DORA (*impressed*) Lights! I dunno...

(*They all stand and look with pleasure at the doll's house.*)

That un in't Post Office'll not have lights, I do know...

9 *Shabby Cottage*

(*Maggie on main street of Little Thraves. As she draws near we see small girl of previous day come out of cottage. Door is left open. Maggie looks curiously in and we see glimpse of bare interior with peeling wallpaper and little furniture.*
Woman comes forward and shuts door. Still pale and depressed looking.
Girl is running ahead.)

10 *Post Office*

(Kate running ahead of Maggie. When she reaches Post Office she stops and stares in window.
Maggie approaches and herself stops at window. Glances sideways and sees that girl is looking at doll's house.
Child's face very pinched and wide-eyed. Hair uncombed. We see Maggie registering alarm that child is gazing at the coveted doll's house.)

MAGGIE Hello.

KATE (*in very small voice*) Hello.

MAGGIE (*trying to sound careless*) Looking at doll's house, are you?

(*Kate nods. Does not move her gaze from doll's house.*)

MAGGIE (*airily, thinking she is being cunning*) Mmmm. 'S'all right, I s'pose. But not really worth money, that's what my Mam says. Says it's nowt but plastic. (*She looks sideways at Kate to see the effect of words. Child's gaze still has not moved.*) Ever had a doll's house, have you? (*Kate shakes head.*) Nor me either. (*In attempt to move Kate's attention.*) What's your name? Mine's Maggie. Maggie Tanner.

KATE (*still uncertainly*) Kate Robinson.

MAGGIE (*being rather grown up and motherly*) Coming to our school are you? Come to live here?

(*Kate nods.*)

Walk along wi' me then, if you like.

(*Kate hesitates.*)

Come *on*...

(*Child walks with her and we see them from rear.*)

11 *School Hall*

(*School assembled waiting expectantly.*)

MRS GARTON ...and now the three kings. Kevin, you'll be the first, and then David. And—we have a new girl today. Kate Robinson. Would you like to be a king Kate?

(*Children all look at Kate.*)

KATE (*almost in whisper*) Yes please, Miss.

MRS GARTON Good. Now, Joseph—Michael, I've chosen you for that. And now there's just Mary. (*Pause*) Maggie Tanner!

MAGGIE (*overjoyed*) Oooh, thank you, Mrs Garton. Thank you. (*Thinks*) It worked! It worked! Oooh—*Mary*...

MRS GARTON And this year, instead of having the Nativity Play in school on the last day of term as usual, we thought we would have it on Christmas Eve itself, and in the Church. (*Little murmur runs through the hall.*) And we thought it would be nice, too, if you saved your little gifts to one another until after the service. These days, people seem to forget what the meaning of Christmas is. It is not really about eating lots of food, and getting lots of presents—nice as it all is. It is not even about Santa Claus. It is about *giving*—just as the three kings gave to the baby Jesus. And this Christmas I want you all to try to remember this especially...

12 *School playground*

(*Sarah and Wendy are in foreground but in background we see Maggie obviously being friendly to Kate—offering her sweets.*)

WENDY My Mam'll be furious. *Never* thought that Maggie Tanner'd get it. Not even pretty.

SARAH Been sucking up to Mrs Garton, she has, all the time. 'Can I give them books out, Mrs Garton? Here's some berries for't nature table, Mrs Garton.' *I* never had to suck up when I was Mary. Course, could've made her Mary 'cos she was *sorry* for her, I s'pose.

(*We see Maggie approach unnoticed by the pair. She*

overhears what they are saying. She then walks slowly away and they are unaware that she has heard.)

WENDY What, her Mum and Dad not having much...

SARAH Being poor. Not got two ha'pence to rub together, the Tanners, my Mam says. And my Dad says that that Ben don't even get proper wages, neither.

WENDY What's he work there for, then?

SARAH (*shrugs*) I dunno. Must be daft. Anyhow, I know what Maggie wants for Christmas. That doll's house, in Post Office. But her Mam'll never get her that. Costs too much. Four pound fifty it is, I've seen it.

WENDY Four pound fifty ain't much. Bikes cost a lot more'n that.

SARAH I keep telling you—poor, they are. Any road, I bet she'll be a really rotten Mary. Bet she don't do it right.

WENDY Bet she drops baby, or summat...

13 *Village*

(*Maggie, Sarah and Wendy on way home.*)

MAGGIE On'y thing is—what about t'donkey.

SARAH What about it?

MAGGIE 'T' *real* donkey, silly. It'll be old enough by then. But on'y thing is—in *church*, see. Don't know if a donkey'll be let come in church.

WENDY (*at once*) Bet it ain't. I bet Mrs Garton'll not let you. It might—(*breaks off and giggles*)—you know...What if it did it on't church floor?

MAGGIE (*scornfully*) Trust *you*, to think o' that...Anyhow, *liked* donkeys Jesus did, so there. Bet *he'd*'ve let it. Going to tell Mrs Garton that, I am.
(*Kate appears in distance.*)

SARAH There's that Kate Robinson. Fancy making her a king! 'S'not fair. Only new, she is, and she's a king, and all I am's a shepherd.

WENDY (*lowering voice slightly, conscious of being about to impart dark secret*) Heard my Mam talking about her Mam. She's going to have a baby. And my Mam says... (*Heads go together as Wendy whispers and others listen, their eyes stretching.*)

MAGGIE (*eyes ahead towards Kate*) Not get many presents then. Not if she ain't got a dad.

WENDY (*smugly*) Roller skates, I'm getting. *And* a bike. What're you? (*She exchanges glances with Sarah.*) (*Maggie does not reply. They goad her further.*)

SARAH I'm getting a new bike, an' all. Got an old un o' course. *And* I'm getting a camera. What did you say you're getting Maggie?

MAGGIE (*hard pressed*) A doll's house. Aye—that's it—a a doll's house. (*The other two again exhange glances*) Yes, I am. (*Maggie looks ahead again at Kate*) Her Mam's baby...What if it's born on Christmas *Day*? It'd be like Jesus. (*Sarah and Wendy both look scandalised.*)

SARAH Oooh, Maggie Tanner! You shouldn't say that!

MAGGIE Why not?

SARAH You shouldn't. You shouldn't say things are like Jesus.

MAGGIE Don't see why not. And Jesus was born in a stable, anyhow, and my Mam says that house they're in ain't fit for a pig to live in. She says it's all...

(*They walk away, still talking.*)

15 *Post Office*

(*Maggie approaches Post Office. She pauses and looks in window at doll's house.*)

MAGGIE (*v/o*) If I wrap it, and put it under a tree in church, they'll never know...No-one'd know... (*She hesitates. Looks again at doll's house.*) On'y thing is, did make a bargain...Mam'll never get me it, I know she won't. But we *ain't* poor, we ain't!

(She pulls out envelope containing five pound note and looks at it. With sudden decision she pushes open the shop door.)

16 *Maggie's House*

TED Knew you would be. Proper good little Mary, you'll be.

DORA It'll be nice having it in church. And Christmas Eve, and all.

MAGGIE Going to ask Mrs Garton tomorrow about donkey. Bet she *will* let us have him, even if 'tis in church. Never had a real donkey afore. Had lambs, but not a donkey.

TED You named him yet, have you, Maggie?

MAGGIE (*shakes head*) Been *thinking*...Been trying to think o' sommat Christmassy...

TED *Call* him Christmas.

MAGGIE (*face lightening*) Never thought o' that! *Do*, that would—Christmas!

DORA Rum name for a donkey, if you ask me.

MAGGIE (*suddenly remembering she has to lay foundations of her plot—with slightly exaggerated nonchalance*) Oooh. And another thing. Mrs Garton says we've to put presents to each other under't tree. (*She gives sideways glance at mother to see effect of words.*) Think I might be getting summat special, this year...

DORA Summat special? Why's that?

MAGGIE (*shrugs*) Oooh, dunno...Seen people whispering and that. Keep giving me funny looks. Just got a feeling, that's all.

TED Told Ben, have you? About Mary?

MAGGIE Just going to. Shan't be long, Mam...

17 *Ben's House*

MAGGIE (*still excited*) ...and afterwards we're to give presents out, Mrs Garton says. So *shall* you, Ben? (*Ben is occupied mending chair and carries on throughout this interchange, not often looking at Maggie at all.*)

BEN Not one for church, Maggie, you know that.

MAGGIE But it's *different* at Christmas! (*Persuasively*) There'll be a tree, an' all. And I mightn't ever be Mary again. Don't suppose I ever shall.

BEN (*changing subject*) Bargain worked, anyhow.

MAGGIE What bargain?

BEN The one you was on about yesterday. All that about bargains.

MAGGIE (*looks somewhat disturbed*) Worked right enough, it did. I'm to be Mary, all right...

(*She watches him for a moment as he works, her face still troubled.*)

Ben...If you make a bargain wi' somebody else, and then break it, that's bad—I know it is. But—if you break a bargain wi' *yourself*, it don't really matter much, does it?

BEN (*impassively, not looking at her*) More, I reckon.

MAGGIE (*genuinely aghast*) *More*? But there's on'y me'd *know*!

BEN That's it. You'd know. You'd not feel right wi' yoursen. Can't cheat and feel right wi' yoursen...

(*Maggie stares at him, dismayed by what he is saying and beginning to realise its truth.*)

18 Maggie's Bedroom

(*Maggie is in bedroom that night. She is in nightdress. Pulls out box containing doll's house from under bed. Gazes at it, but does not attempt to open it.*)

MAGGIE (*to herself*) *Was* cheating, in a way, I s'pose... (*Brightens*) But not really...How'd *I* know I'd get that five pound? Never've *made* a bargain, in first place, if I'd've known that was coming...And if I do put it under tree, Mam and Dad'll think some of 'em have clubbed up together...

(*She sighs and pushes box back under bed and parts*

curtains and looks out of window.)
(*v/o*) No snow...not yet...sky's clear...more like frost'n snow...
(*Pause*)
Wonder how big star *was*—star o' Bethlehem? *That* un's big...That un, and all...How did they *know*, them shepherds? Couldn't've...
(*Voices outside below. Ted and Ben are crossing the yard.*)

MAGGIE (*aloud*) *Lambing*! Ooooh, there'll be lambs for Christmas!
(*She knocks excitedly on window. The men pause and look up at window and raise arms in salute. She waves back. They enter pens.*) Ooooooh!
(*She throws herself back on bed then climbs in and pulls blankets up to chin.*) (*Thinks*) Lucky you are, Maggie Tanner. Poor, them two said we were. *Are* we poor? Don't *feel* poor...*They* are, though right enough...
(*We see Maggie's face troubled as she remembers Kate's face pressed against the shop window, looking at the doll's house, and then clearing as she shakes off thoughts.*) Best Christmas ever, this'll be...(*She shuts her eyes.*)

19 *Shabby House*

(*Fade up to Maggie, Sarah and Wendy carol singing outside Robinsons' house. They finish and giggle and Sarah bangs on door. Door is opened by Kate. We see mother beyond her in poorly furnished room. Wendy & Sarah stare and Wendy nudges Sarah and they recollect themselves and chant. We see that twigs have been pushed into a jug to make a Christmas tree and Kate has been making decorations with bits of coloured paper and foil.*)

MAGGIE/SARAH/WENDY (*together*)
Christmas is coming,
The goose is getting fat,

Please to put a penny in the old man's hat,
If you haven't got a penny, a ha'penny will do,
If you haven't got a ha'penny, God bless you!

(*Kate looks inquiringly at her mother as chant stops. Mother grudgingly takes up purse and delves into it and gives Kate a coin which she in turn passes to Sarah. We see Sarah's face, then her palm, where a twopence piece lies. Maggie senses Kate's embarrassment.*)

MAGGIE (*impulsively*) *You* like to come carol singing wi' us, would you? We've rest o' Main Street to do yet!

MOTHER (*sharply & instantly*) She ain't going carol singing. Not having begging. Not come to that.

MAGGIE Oh, 's'not *begging*, Mrs Robinson. It's for Charity. It's for *poor* children—you know, that ain't got no Mums and...(*Her voice trails off as she realises what she's saying.*)

MOTHER (*tight lipped*) She's not coming. Shut door, Kate, it's blowing in.

(*Kate shuts door. The three look at one another then move slowly away.*)

WENDY Rude thing! And look at that—two p! Three verses they had, an' all!

SARAH See that tree? Call that a Christmas tree? Just a few old twigs wi' bits o' milk bottle tops and—

MAGGIE (*stopping in her tracks*) Shut up! Shut up, both of you!

(*They stare at her.*)

SARAH What's up wi' you?

MAGGIE She'd *like* a Christmas tree, o' course she would, same as you and me! And presents—bikes and that. It's mean talking like that.

WENDY (*ashamed of herself but on defensive nonetheless*) Oooh, hark at goody goody. Thinks because she's Mary she ought to have a halo. Still, I daresay you know how she feels.

MAGGIE What d'you mean?

WENDY (*shrugs*) Oh—nothing. Better get off home,

Mary, or your halo'll fall off.

MAGGIE (*furiously*) I *will* get off. You're mean, rotten mean, both of you!

(*She runs off under lamplight and others watch her go.*)

SARAH Thinks she's everyone, just because she's Mary. What did you mean—about Maggie knowing how Kate feels?

WENDY (*confidentially*) You know that doll's house—one in Post Office,—one I said she wanted?

SARAH It's gone. I saw it had. Maybe her Mam *has* got it for her...

WENDY (*shaking her head*) Her. Maggie. *She* bought it.

SARAH (*astonished*) Her?

WENDY (*nodding*) And you know what I bet she's going to do? I bet she's going to put it in Church, under't tree, wi' her name on it, so's everyone'll think...

21 *The fields*

(*Maggie is going over fields to village, carrying box.*)

22 *Churchyard*

(*Maggie goes up the path and Wendy and Sarah are hiding behind a tombstone.*)

SARAH (*in whisper*) Sssh! Here she comes!

WENDY (*triumphantly*) There you are! Told you! She's got it!

23 *Church*

(*Maggie enters church. She stands and takes in stillness. We hear echoing footsteps as she approaches Christmas tree and with a last look round to make sure no one is looking, places box at foot of tree with other parcels. She looks at it, smiles, and tiptoes out.*)

24 *Churchyard*

(Maggie goes down the path and leaves.)

WENDY Come on Sarah, let's go and look!

25 *Church*

(Sarah kneels at the foot of the tree in the church and looks at the tag. A look of utter disbelief comes on her face.)

SARAH *(in churchy whisper)* Wendy—look!

(Wendy too crouches over and looks and they exchange surprised and somewhat shamed glances.)

26 *Church*

(The assembly is taking place.)

MRS GARTON And it's important at Christmas to remember that this story is still alive. It is not just a story of something that happened nearly two thousand years ago in a far off country. It is still alive today, in our hearts.

(Shot of Maggie's face.)

And so, while we tell again the wonderful story of the birth of Jesus, I want you all to remember this, and for 'Bethlehem'—read 'Little Thraves'...

1ST CHILD And she brought forth her first born son. And wrapped him in swaddling clothes, and laid him in a manger; because there was no room for them at the inn.

(Congregation looks at Kate's mother)

And there were in the same country shepherds, abiding in the fields, keeping watch over their flocks by night. And lo, the angel of the Lord came upon them, and the glory of the Lord shone round about them, and they were sore afraid. And the angel said unto them: *(Angel steps forwards with arms upraised before shepherds. One of shepherds has live lamb. We see Ben's face watching this.*)

2ND CHILD Fear not, for behold I bring you good tidings of great joy, which shall be unto all people. For unto you is born this day in the city of David a Saviour, which is Christ the Lord. And this shall be a sign unto you. You shall find the babe wrapped in swaddling clothes, lying in a manger. (*Maggie smiles. Dora, Ted & Ben exchanging looks that are both proud and pleased, despite themselves.*)

1ST CHILD And suddenly there was with the angel a multitude of the heavenly host, praising God and saying:

CONGREGAT: Glory to God in the highest, and on earth peace, good will toward men.

1ST CHILD And it came to pass, as the angels were gone away from them into heaven, the shepherds said one to another:

SHEPHERDS (*in unison*) Let us now go even unto Bethlehem and see this thing which is come to pass, which the Lord has made known unto us. And they came and found Mary, and Joseph, and the babe lying in a manger.

(*Shepherds move toward central group. One of them carries live lamb.*)

(*Singing*)
What shall I give him,
Poor as I am?
If I were a shepherd, I would give a lamb.
(*Kate shyly approaches in king's costume.*)
If I were a wise man,
I would do my part
Yet what shall I give him?
Give my heart.

3RD CHILD Then Herod, when he had privily called the wise men, inquired of them diligently what time the star appeared. And he sent them to Bethlehem, and said:

HEROD Go, and search diligently for the young child and when you have found him, bring me word again, that I may come and worship him there.

3RD CHILD When they had heard the king, they departed and lo, the star, which they saw in the sky, went before them, till it came and stood over where the young child was. When they saw the star they rejoiced with exceeding great joy. And when they were come unto Mary his mother, they fell down and worshipped him, and when they had opened their treasures, they gave unto him gifts, gold, and frankinsense, and myrrh.

(*The congregation or children sing 'We Three Kings'. Kate is the last king to present her gift to Mary. As she approaches with her gift, Mary smiles radiantly at Kate, who remains solemn and scared-looking. Ted and Dora glance sideways half-smiling at one another. As the congregation sings 'O, Come All Ye Faithful' Mrs Garton hands out the parcels from beneath the tree. A king takes two small parcels to Maggie, from Sarah and Wendy. Maggie looks surprised, and Sarah and Wendy smile sheepishly. Then Mrs Garton picks up the doll's house and reads the tag on the parcel: 'To Kate with love at Christmas'. We see Kate's astounded face as she realises it is for her.*)

HELEN CRESSWELL

Personal Essay

This play was commissioned by BBC Television, and so its structure was obviously dictated to some extent by the medium. I have never written for stage, (though I did adapt *Lizzie Dripping* for the Unicorn Theatre), but I imagine that it would be more difficult. Television offers a marvellous fluidity of both time and place, scenes are short, different strands can be woven simultaneously without any jarring.

In this particular play, for instance, it is necessary that we actually *see* the loving care Maggie's parents are spending on the making of her doll's house—that the viewer is let into the secret that it is there, waiting for her. It is vital, too, that we are shown the poorness of Kate's surroundings, that we understand how much of a real miracle it would be for *her* to have a doll's house for Christmas.

Then there is another secret, this time between Maggie and the viewer. We know, as Maggie's parents and Ben do not, that Maggie has bought herself the doll's house in the village shop.

The length of this play is 25 minutes. For all its scenes to be included in a stage performance, the curtain would be going up and down like a yo-yo.

In writing this piece I have much wanted a pastoral setting, with sheep—echoes of the shepherds in the fields, and a dark country sky where stars are visible. Effortlessly and swiftly achieved on film—very difficult to establish on stage.

Another thing I like about television is that we can see into the mind, we can hear thoughts. This can be achieved by the use of voice-over—that is, seeing Maggie's face, while hearing her voice saying what she is thinking. Alternatively, she can actually speak her thoughts out loud when she is alone. This is really the TV equivalent of the stage soliloquy, and is a time-honoured device, but it can be achieved quite unobtrusively on television, whereas it tends to jar, and seem stagey and artificial, in a theatre.

As a writer of TV drama for children, I am very much in favour of voice-over as a technique. It seems to me very important, because children are, after all, fairly powerless. They often take a great deal from the adults in their lives in the way of criticism, and only rarely dare they answer back—except in thought! They have secret hopes that they never tell. The voice-over allows us to share them, and so to understand the child better.

In this particular case, it is hard to see how the viewer could understand the secret 'bargain' Maggie makes with herself other than by the use of voice-over. Such bargains, (and we have all made them as children, and still sometimes make them as adults), are by their very nature intensely private. And we must know about this bargain in order to understand Maggie's thought processes. She trades playing Mary against the doll's house. Once she has achieved her wish to be Mary, she knows in her bones that to have the doll's house as well would be cheating, even if she herself was the only one who would know.

And so she gives the coveted doll's house to Kate. She does the right thing, painful as it is, without knowing (as we know) that her reward is already waiting for her.

For Bethlehem, Read Little Thraves seems simple enough in terms of theme. But the complexities of Maggie's desires and emotions are such that I feel that this is very clearly a play that would work only on television.

(Or radio, of course. But that is another matter...)

F*ollow On*

Jackie's First Day

Before Reading

- How well do you remember your first day at Secondary School? Who was the first teacher you met? Can you remember any fellow pupils who you met for the first time? Were you nervous? Had you heard 'horror' stories about what happened to new pupils at the school? Were they true? What was your first lesson like? How clearly can you remember that day?

  Working with a partner, preferably one who did not go to the same junior or middle school as you, talk about the most vivid memories you have of that first day. After ten minutes, during which time both of you should have shared experiences, tell the rest of the class some of the memories *your partner* had. Are there any members of the class who remember the same things?

During Reading

- Stop at the point where Mr Bates completes his delivery of the timetable. Check in a dictionary the meaning of the word 'parody'. Is Mr Bates a parody? What point is the writer making here?

After Reading

- In his 'Apology,' Phil Lowe says that his aim was to write a play for junior school pupils in which he made fun of the fears they had about moving to the big school. Examine his play in detail. Pick out the possible problems which he confronts. Does he succeed in making light of these fears?

- Imagine your class was going to perform this play for a nearby junior school or middle school. Write a letter to the headteacher offering to present the play. You must describe the play and explain its purpose.

- Working in pairs, one of you tell the other how to get from your present room to any one of the following parts of the school:
  the hall
  the staffroom
  the main office

the caretaker's room
the music room.

Using the above list, but choosing a different part of the school, swap round and provide similar directions, but this time imagine the other person is totally new to the school. You will find you must now describe things in much more detail.

- Again working with your partner, explain the way in which your school timetable operates. Assume the other person has no knowledge of the school. You must cover such things as the times of the lessons, tutor periods, arrangements for assemblies and lunch, etc. Your partner should ask questions if you fail to explain something clearly.

- Write an information sheet for the new first years. They will receive it before arriving at school. You might like to include such points as the differences between the schools, advice for finding their way around, where to go for assistance, what equipment they will need, new subjects they are likely to take and the facilities available. You should always seek to reassure your reader. Remember you are attempting to ease any anxieties they might have.

- As an alternative to the above, imagine you have been asked to speak to the new first years on their first day in the school. Write this speech.

- Jackie meets four teachers in the course of the play: the Geography teacher who doesn't know his way around the place, the timetabler who manages to get everyone confused, the scatter-brained teacher, and the headmaster who is a mixture of the three. Phil Lowe might easily have written about other 'types' of teacher. In pairs write a scene for the play in which Jackie meets one more teacher. Read this through together and then to the rest of the class.

  You might like to try one of the following:
  —P.E. teacher
  —Drama teacher
  —science teacher
  —head of year

  Do you think teachers differ in their character according to the subject they teach?

- Can you think of any other need for 'Super First Year' in a school? Write a short story in which the cloaked crusader rights other wrongs.

- 'Super First Year' has become the 'agony aunt' for a national newspaper. She has promised to answer all letters relating to schools. Each member of the class should write a letter to her detailing their problem. Working in groups of three of four, compose the most appropriate reply to each of the letters. To start you off, here is one she received in an earlier postbag:

Dear Super First Year,

I don't know which way to turn. All the pupils in this school are horrible. There's too much work to do. The teachers are horrible. The school is horrible. I'm sorry I came here. I want to go back to my Junior School where I was happy. I think that if I went back I'd do much better there. Do you think they would let me back?

Yours sincerely,

A Fifth Year.

- Design a 'This School Is Protected By Super First Year' poster for the main school noticeboard.

- Working in groups of five or six (you'll need to double up on some of the characters) act this play out.

Feet

Before Reading

- What causes you most stress or embarrassment? List the five most stressful things you can think of. For instance, for some of us a job interview might be a really awful experience to have to go through, for others being asked to speak to a large group of people might be worse. Try to choose things which you have actually experienced—after all, we don't get trapped in a lift with a mad axeman every day of the week! When you have compiled your own list compare it with your partner's. Are there any similarities? See if you can agree on *one* particular difficult experience. How does your choice compare with those made by the rest of the class?

- If you don't play tennis yourself, ask a friend what is meant by a 'foot fault'. Nothing to do with tennis, but try and find out what a 'Pyrrhic victory' is—it may not be in your dictionary so you may have to search through other reference books in the school library to find out.

During Reading

- Divide a page of your notebook into four vertical columns. Write down the following names at the top:

  Jane Turner / Alan Carson / Michael Collier / Miss Truman

- As you read through the play jot down the main points you

notice about these characters. For example under Jane you might note that she is embarrassed because Alan used to babysit for her.

- Watch out for any difficult situations Jane Turner gets into, and make a note of how she copes with them.

- Stop reading at the point where Diane says,'You didn't think he was after *you*, did you? (Giggles)' (Page 23). What do you think Jane is thinking at this moment? What can she say to her friends?

After Reading

- Look at the description of the Centre Court at Jane's school (Page 12). Notice the use both girls make of comparisons—the asphalt is compared to Ryvita, the covering of algae to mould on cheese. Write *two* descriptions of sports areas in your own school: the first from the official school handbook for new parents, the second from a letter of complaint by a concerned parent. If you are very daring you might attempt to write about the *same* area of the school in both cases. Try to think of comparisons to make your writing more vivid.

- At first I though Jan Mark had made a typing error in her word 'Ululates' (Page 13). She hasn't, I've checked. If you have never heard the word before try and guess what it could mean. Look at the context... 'Me Carson, you Jane'... When all the class has made an attempt check in a good dictionary and see how close you were.

- Imagine you are Alan Carson. You are writing to a close friend. Describe the tennis match between Mills and Collier. It is important to *be* Carson. What sort of a person is he? Would he give a very serious account? How sympathetic would he be towards Collier? What are his feelings for Jane?

- Write a report of the tennis tournament for the school magazine.

- This play was originally a short story (in *Love You, Hate You, Just Don't Know,* Evans Brothers, 1980; or *Feet and Other Stories,* Kestrel Books, 1983). If you are able to get a copy, compare the two. In this extract from the story, Jane is the narrator:

> *'So anyway, I got rid of all my ladies' doubles and sat around waiting for a mixed doubles. It was cold and windy on Centre Court since it wasn't noon in June, and I wished I had worn a sweater instead of trying to look attractive sort of in short sleeves. Sort of is right. That kind of thing doesn't fool anyone. I had these sandals too which let the draught in something rotten. I should have worn wellies. No one would have noticed. Nobody looks at feet.'*

Find the section in the play covering the extract. In small groups compare the two accounts. Does Jan Mark manage to cover all the above short story extract in her drama script? What are the differences between the two? Which is the most effective?

- If Collier had been the narrator in Jan Mark's short story, how might he have described the tennis match? Write about a side of A4 from his point of view and read it out to the class when it is complete.

- Is *Feet* a good title for the play? Give your reasons.

- Working with a partner, rewrite part of *Feet* in the form of a comic strip. One of you might do the drawing, the other fill in the bubbles. Try dividing the play into sections and allocating each section to each pair, to form a full comic which you can display in your classroom.

- Using a tape recorder and working in pairs, improvise your own sports commentary for the radio. It can be any sport from netball to snooker. Very often sports commentators work in pairs, one describes the action as it develops with the other providing an expert analysis when the opportunity presents itself. You might like to try it that way.

- In her personal essay, Jan Mark writes of sometimes being able to 'lay a bad memory to rest by using it in a story'. Do you feel it is possible to make a painful memory less painful by talking or writing about it? Discuss this as a class. When you have considered this, read again what she says about writing 'fiction, not autobiography'. Discuss this in small groups.

- Write your own script based on a sporting event. Base it as much as possible on real life.

- How important is it to 'play the game for its own sake' or to 'be a good sport'? Is winning the most important thing? Do we take sport too seriously? Write a short essay outlining your views on sport.

Mm

Before Reading

- Have you ever had to say goodbye to a best friend who is moving house? Are your friends still the same as they were when you were in junior school? How reliable are your friends? Do you have any friends of the opposite sex? In pairs, talk about the subject of friendship. Try and decide what it is that makes a true friend. Write a list of the qualities that a 'best friend' should have—does everyone in the class agree?

- Still working with your partner, tell each other about the most memorable experience you have ever had with a friend. Try and describe what you felt like at the time and explain why you have chosen that particular experience.

During Reading

- As you read through the script make a note of any scenes which would make good cartoons. For example, one possibility could be the view David has through the window as his mother prepares to attack his father after she has recovered from her choking fit. At the end of the play discuss your choices with the rest of the class and each draw one cartoon.

- Stop at the point where Matthew Wilder falls off his bike. What sort of a lad is he?

- Stop at the point at which Lucy-Ann and David wave farewell to Allen. Did you suspect their relationship was going to develop? Are there any 'clues' in the play that suggested this was going to happen? Predict how the play is going to end.

After Reading

- What was it that David found in the cupboard?

- The play is, in one sense, about pairs of relationships. Consider the following pairs: David/Allen; David/Lucy-Ann; Mr and Mrs Hannigan; Joe/Pete, the two removal men; the giant/Mrs Bernard. In small groups discuss these relationships.

- How far is it true to say that the readers/audience seem to understand what is going on rather more that the characters?

- Working through the play, list any examples of humour and say why they are comic.

- Re-reading the play for this Follow On section, I am conscious of having been a little mean towards Pete, the removal man. Surely he would have lost his temper at some stage in the day! Working in pairs discuss what could have happened. Where might it have fitted into the script? Write the scene in pairs, and then act out the different possibilities in class.

- Mrs Hannigan and Lucy-Ann only meet for a moment at the end of the play. Imagine that Mrs Hannigan had asked Lucy-Ann to tea. How would the two get on? Would the girl continue to have such a high regard for David's mother? In groups of four (David and his father are there too) improvise this meeting.

- We do not see David/Allen/Matthew/Lucy-Ann in school but it would be interesting to read their school reports. Write a report for *two* of the characters.

- Allen has moved to Birmingham and writes letters to both David and Lucy-Ann. Write a short story in the form of an exchange of letters among the three. You need not add a commentary. Allow the letters themselves to 'tell' the story. There are a lot of questions left unanswered in the play. What has happened to Mrs Bernard and the giant? How are David and Lucy-Ann getting on? Do they confess to Allen that they are seeing each other? How friendly will Lucy-Ann be to Allen? Try to reflect the characters of the three in your letters.

- I'm not entirely sure I have chosen the right title for the script. *Mm* seems awfully short when I see it printed out. Of course, it's too late to change things now, but there are alternatives. One way of choosing a title that I've found useful in the past is to write the story, play, or poem and *then* to decide on the best title. Very often this is a quotation from the writing which seems to sum everything up. Decide on five other possible titles for this play, using quotations from the script.

- Draw a sketch of each of the main characters. Underneath write down a quotation from the script that you think most accurately sums up their personality.

- In pairs, improvise any of the following telephone conversations:
Allen to Lucy-Ann (from Birmingham);
Mrs Hannigan to Mrs Bernard (about a proposed visit to Birmingham by David);
Johnny Brown to Mrs Hannigan (about David going to tea);
David to Allen (in Birmingham);
the giant to Mrs Bernard;
the two removal men (the van has broken down on the motorway and Mrs Bernard and the giant are waiting at the new house);
the two'giant' brothers (they are talking about the incident where Allen was dangled over the water)

- If you had to act out one of the roles which would it be?

- When writing the play I deliberately tried to create 'echoes'—words, phrases or situations which recur during the play. For instance, the play starts with David being told to 'Calm down' by his mother. At the end Lucy-Ann is telling the boy to do the exact same thing. Collect examples of this repetition. What effect does this have? Why is it written in this way?

- The tone of the play is light-hearted. However, as I have confessed in the personal essay, the original intention was to write a more serious short story. The seeds of this are here: quarrelling between the Hannigans; a best friend moving away; arguments between the two boys over Lucy-Ann; the blossoming romance between Mrs Bernard and the giant, etc. Choose one incident in the script and rewrite it as though it were deadly serious. Use the short story form and try to show what the characters involved are thinking.

Naughty Girls

Before Reading

- *Naughty Girls* is a radio play. In groups, discuss the differences between a play for radio and a play for television.

- A radio play like this needs to be read out properly if it is to succeed. Some of the lines must be practised in advance before read out. Read the play to yourself first. The script is great fun to read but you must put your life and soul into it! Don't be afraid to exaggerate the voices and sound effects.

  In the interview which follows the play, Rony Robinson tells would-be readers to pick up the cues very quickly and say their lines immediately the previous speaker has finished, 'if not earlier'. Remember this advice when you read the play out loud.

During Reading

- Ask yourself whether there is a structure to the play. Are there any definite scenes? Does a play like *Naughty Girls* need a definite sense of order?

- Does *Naughty Girls* remind you of anything on television or radio?

After Reading

- There are some obvious jokes here: 'Mark my words', says Miss Grindle. 'Three out of ten, Miss' reply the girls. What are the funniest moments in the script?

- Could *Naughty Girls* have worked as a television play? Discuss this with a partner. If you feel it could, list the changes which would need to take place. If you feel it is only suitable as a radio play, explain your reasons.

- Design a poster for the play. Try and capture the atmosphere.

- In his 'interview', Rony Robinson talks about how he wrote the play. Read this again and in your own words write his advice down as though it were a couple of paragraphs taken from an information sheet with the title, 'How To Write Your Own Book'.

- I'm not sure how serious Rony Robinson is when he says in his 'interview' that shopkeepers complained about this play. Do you think it is rude about people in authority? Is there any harm in making fun of, say, your teachers in a school magazine or a school play? Discuss this as a class.

● Miss Grindle tunes in to various radio stations during the play. In small groups of three or four, work out your own short extracts from programmes which might have appeared in the script. Try to cover different types of programmes. For instance, you might create another advertising jingle, a 'heavy' news programme, a radio phone-in, a sports report, a schools' educational programme, or a Citizen's Band (CB) network. If possible, record these on tape.

● Assuming the Inspector escapes drowning, he will have to make out an official report on Miss Grindle's lesson. Fill in the following form.

INSPECTOR'S REPORT ON VISIT TO .... SCHOOL
DATE.................TEACHER ....
SUBJECT ....

1 *Brief description of lesson*

....
....
....
....
....

2 *Relationship between teacher and pupils*

....
....
....

3 *Action to be taken by Local Authority/School*

....
....
....

● All schools are visited at some time by VIPs. Recently, my own school had a flying visit by a member of the royal family and suddenly we found that roofs (she flew in by helicopter!) and woodwork were repaired and an old building which happened to be near the landing site was given a long overdue coat of paint. I'm not sure whether this was coincidence or not but it certainly brightened the place up. In *Naughty Girls* the School Inspector's arrival sparks off a whole new imaginative approach by the teacher as she tries to impress him. It all goes terribly wrong. Write your own story of what might take place if a Very Important Person were to visit your school. Give it the title, 'The Visit'.

● Look carefully at the script. Notice how the writer has created a sense of excitement and pace by his use of quick-fire dialogue. The play really rattles along in parts. Work with a partner and write a comedy sketch for two people. If you are in need of an idea use one of the following potentially comic situations:

a) An employee from the Council arrives to ask you to leave your house as it is due to be demolished.
b) You meet a person who seems to know you well. You haven't a clue who he or she is, but don't wish to appear stupid.
c) You would like your boss to give you an increase in pay but are too polite to actually come out and ask for it directly. Your boss is rather mean.
d) You are on the twenty-first floor of an office block. You see a person on the window-sill who is considering whether or not to jump off it to test a newly designed parachute made out of the daily newspaper
e) Your meal is absolutely awful and you call for the waiter/waitress to make a complaint. Unfortunately the waiter/waitress has a hearing problem.

Act out the sketch.

- Have you got a favourite comedy show on television? Write a scene or sketch for it.

How Mavis met Gary Blood

Before Reading

- *How Mavis Met Gary Blood* is a sequel to *Naughty Girls* (although it actually covers events which happened before the Inspector visited the school). Very often television will 'pilot' a single programme, often in the form of a TV film or play, to test the audience's reaction. If this is favourable a series is made. Working in groups of three or four, discuss Rony Robinson's plays and decide whether or not there is the basis for a series here. Can you suggest possible ideas for story-lines? Would the series work on television? Which characters would you wish to retain?

- It is sometimes said that sequels are never as good as the originals. Do you agree? Refer to examples from television, films and books.

During Reading

- Rony Robinson's plays tear along at a great pace and it is possible to miss some of the jokes. My personal favourite occurs at the end of Scene 4 when Mavis' mother criticises newspapers for not being able to spell correctly even when they're talking. As you read the play make a note of what you consider to be the funniest jokes.

- Anything to do with pop music dates very quickly. When Mr Big lists the pop singers and groups that he 'owns', he uses thinly disguised names of existing artists; or at least they were 'thinly disguised' when the play was first written. See if you can work out the real names. You may well have to ask your teacher! Update the play by making your own suggestions for current pop singers but disguising their names.

After Reading

- Having read the play, do you think *How Mavis Met Gary Blood* is as good as *Naughty Girls*?
- In one sense there is a play within a play here. Does the Gary Blood/Socko Sausages play benefit from being within the Miss Grindle/Naughty Girls framework?
- Mr Big would like some further ideas for his latest Socko Sausages competition. Using one side of A4 paper, design the newspaper advert for your own competition.
- In this play Mr Big and the naughty girls fail to meet up with each other. This seems a shame. Assuming Mavis was, in fact, telling the truth and Mr Big does exist, imagine what would happen if he had been asked to distribute the prizes at the school's end of year prize evening. Write your own short script.
- Miss Grindle gives some advice to her girls on the art of talking or writing.

'You have to describe things, paint pictures with language. It's no good saying "then" and then "then". Use words.'

And again:

'Make the most of your tale. Tell us in the language of Shakespeare. Use words.'

Choose one part of this script and rewrite it in the way suggested by Miss Grindle. You will notice, of course, that when Mavis does this she exaggerates tremendously.

- Mavis enters a perfectly silly competition in order to meet Gary Blood. Have you ever met a famous person? Was he or she like you had imagined they would be? Why do people queue up for hours for what is all too often a very fleeting glimpse of their idol? Is there someone you would really like to meet?
- What exactly does it mean to be famous? To help you answer this question, make a list of the ten most famous people in the world. Compare your list with those of the rest of the class. Have you any names in common? Do you notice any common features? In ten years time would your lists be likely to change much? Are the most famous people necessarily the most popular?

Would you like to be famous?

For Bethlehem, Read Little Thraves

Before Reading

- Helen Cresswell's play is set in a small rural community. If you are to read it out easily you will have to understand how the spelling and punctuation of words (especially the use of the apostrophe) is influenced by the dialect spoken in this part of Northern England. We associate different accents with different parts of the world; for example, people from Canada, Australia, Birmingham, the West Indies or Devon will all have quite distinct ways of speaking. Discuss the subject of accents as a class. Are there any words you use which you think are peculiar to your part of the country? Have you got an accent? Do any of your teachers have a different accent? How many regional accents do you hear on television or radio? What is meant by 'Standard English'?

- *For Bethlehem, Read Little Thraves* is a film script, and as such the writer has to give a lot of information to the director. In the original version Helen Cresswell used technical terms often in abbreviated form. In order to make it easier to read I have edited these out for *Scriptz*. However it might be interesting for you to see a section of the script as originally sent to the BBC. As you read, compare it with the edited version. What are the differences?

  The extract covers the play's final moments:

Congregation or children only sing 'We three kings' throughout this scene. We see presentation of gifts. Kate is the last of the three kings. We see her in c/u from Maggie's point of view. As Kate approaches with gift Maggie smiles radiantly at her, but she remains solemn and scared-looking.

(*Interpose shot of Kate staring at doll's house in window.*)

Then cut to Kate holding out gift. As Maggie takes it and smiles we see again shot of parcel lying under tree. Maggie's whole face is lit with joy.
C/u Ben, Ted and Dora. They glance sideways half-smiling at one another.

(*Vaseline shot of Ben's doll's house all lit up.*)

Fade. Fade Hymn.
Congretation sings 'O come all ye Faithful', Fade up to closing hymn. One child hands up parcels from under tree. Mrs Garton hands them to three kings who then take them to recipients. We see one king take two small parcels to Maggie. She looks surprised then looks at Sarah and Wendy who smile sheepishly. Then we see Mrs Garton pick up doll's house parcel. Maggie, still in tableau, watches

intently. C/u tag on parcel: to Kate with love at Christmas. Shot of Kate taking parcel and her astounded face as she realises it is for her.
Begin to roll titles.
Shot of Kate's mother, astounded
Congregation begin to leave church.

Scene 31 Int. Eve. Church
Interior church with congregation singing 'O Little Town of Bethlehem'.

Scene 32 Ext. Day. Fields.
Aerial sıhot snow covered fields and sheep lying in them.

Scene 33 Ext. Day. Signpost
C/u snow covered sign: 'Little Thraves'

- Can you work out what these abbreviations taken from the original TV script mean? In each case remember that they are instructions for a camera or tape recorder.

EXT (or INT)
F/X
tracks
Z/I
SHOT
mix
CU
Fade
LS
V/O
CUT
VASELINE SHOT

During Reading

- Stop after reading the directions at the beginning of Scene 8: 'Ben is fetching something out of large cupboard. Ted goes over.' What do you think he has hidden there?

- Stop at beginning of Scene 10 at the point where the directions tell us that Kate 'Stares in window'. What do you suppose she is looking at?

- Read on a little and when you have checked your answer predict how the play will end. Remember, this is a play for Christmas.

- Stop at end of Scene 25. Why Sarah and Wendy so surprised?

After Reading

- This play is about Christmas although many of you reading it will not yourselves be Christians. When an anthology like *Scriptz* is put together lots of people (pupils/teachers/parents) are asked their opinion of the contents. This play was universally popular although one reviewer did pose the question, 'Might this play only be suitable for those youngsters who are Christians and attend Church?' This is a fair point. What do you think? Working in small groups consider the reviewer's question and work out your own response to it.

- Two other reviewers had interesting reactions:
  'I like the play even though it's a bit young for me!'
  (fourteen year old)
  'It's a magical play—it really brought back those innocent days of early childhood!' (forty-ish teacher)

What is your opinion?

- *Scriptz* is an anthology of humorous plays. *For Bethlehem, Read Little Thraves* is certainly not intended as a series of jokes. So, in what way does Helen Cresswell's play use humour?

- At the beginning of the nativity play, Mrs Garton says that the story of Christmas is 'still alive in us today'. Bearing in mind the title of the play, how does Helen Cresswell manage to convey the spirit of Christmas?

- Is the play too sentimental? Do people really behave as generously as Maggie? In groups discuss this question. You would be well advised to read what Helen Cresswell herself has to say on this matter towards the end of her personal essay.

- Look at the use of directions. Helen Cresswell carefully describes certain moments which she wants the film director to cover. In her personal essay the writer says, 'it is necessary that we actually *see* the loving care Maggie's parents are spending on the making of her doll's house'. In groups, examine the play for similar visual incidents which you feel are important in the play. Helen Cresswell gives a reason why the above scene is necessary. Try and do the same for the examples you choose.

- One method that film makers often use is 'montage'—that is, selecting, cutting and piecing together seperate shots. For example, a scene from a film about a bank robbery might have the following series of shots:

1 A shot of the inside of the bank's vault with the employees stacking sacks of money onto a trolley.
2 A well-dressed customer at the counter deliberately allowing someone to overtake him in the queue.
3 A car pulling up alongside an armoured security van.
4 The trolley loaded with money being wheeled along the corridor.
5 The customer, now at the front of the queue, searching for his

wallet and the cashier becoming impatient.
6 A row beginning to develop between the security van's driver and the driver of the car which is illegally parked.
7 Two young women walking quickly towards the bank and placing masks on their faces.

You can probably guess the rest! Prepare your own sequence of shots to suit one of the following selection of films:

a) A roasting hot day in a film about a sporting event.
b) A film about a child who becomes separated from his or her parents in a crowded store.
c) A scene from a romantic film where the two lovers meet for the first time.
d) A home for the elderly in a documentary about the plight of the elderly.
e) A charity appeal for the starving people of the developing world.
f) A news report about the preparations for a major outdoors pop music festival.

- The personal essay also covers the writer's use of voice-over. Discuss with your teacher just what is meant by the word 'soliloquy' then look again at Scene 23. Imagine Helen Cresswell had used voice-over here. Write what you think Maggie might have said at this point in the play. When you have finished do the same again, but this time choose your own scene.

- Very often the BBC or ITV will send schools a pamphlet about forthcoming schools' programmes. Write a one page publicity feature for this pamphlet on Helen Cresswell's play.

- There are other religious festivals in the year which are celebrated in British schools. These include the Muslim festival of Eid ul-Fitr, the West Indian Carnival, the Chinese New Year and the Hindu festival of Diwali. Using either the school or public library, research these festivals. Prepare a short talk for the class on one of them.

- It is the first day back after the Christmas holidays. Sarah, Wendy and Maggie are walking home from school. They are discussing the Nativity play. Using the same format as in the script, write this scene.

Television Commercials: Extended Study

'...it's time for me to take a break for the adverts to persuade you to buy things you don't want with money you haven't got.' (Radio announcer in Rony Robinson's *Naughty Girls*).

Scriptz contains examples of television scripts. Sometimes, however, it is the short scripts between the official programmes that I find most interesting. TV commercials can be thoroughly entertaining and they are always well made—not surprising given that the cost of even a few seconds is reckoned in many thousands of pounds. An advertiser has perhaps twenty to thirty seconds to present the particular product in as favourable a light as possible. At the same time they have to entertain—no firm wants their product associated with a boring commercial.

Humour is often used to sell a product. Here is a script for Brook Bond's Chicken Oxo. You will certainly have seen the Oxo family on television. This has been one of the most successful, long-running advertising campaigns in the history of television. I suspect that the writer, Douglas Adams, was referring to this when he wrote that the commercials seek to show 'how a perfectly ordinary stock cube could form the natural focus of a normal, happy family life.' (*The Long Dark Tea-Time of the Soul*, Heinemann)

The script is divided into 'Vision' and 'Sound'. In commercials vision is often more important than speech.

Client BROOKE BOND OXO
Title 'TURKISH'
Length 30 SECONDS

Product CHICKEN OXO
Medium TV

VISION	**SOUND**
	½ second silence
Open on the Oxo family round the table in the kitchen. There is a post-Christmas air about the kitchen, with decorations still hanging up. Nick is wearing a 'joke' face with specs and a big nose. Alison laughs at him. Mum brings a dish to the table. Jason rushes to sit down at the table for the meal.	General family hubbub throughout.

Cut to ECU of a slice of pastry crust being lifted from a turkey and ham pie.

Cut to CU of Dad speaking to Mum.

DAD: Smells good. Ham?

Cut to CU of Mum as if she is expecting criticism. She smiles towards Dad.

MUM: Turkey and ham.

Cut back to Dad looking a bit disappointed at the prospect of more turkey.

DAD: Oh. Turkey.

ECU of a Chicken Oxo pack with some cubes being shaken out.

Cut to Mum delivering another dish to the family table.

MUM: Turkey risotto?
ALISON: Oh good!

Cut to Jason peering at the dish being placed on the table before him. He glances round the table at the reaction of the family to his pun.

JASON: Ah good! I was feeling a bit peckish!

ALISON: Oh what a foul joke.
NICK: Oh dear, oh dear.

ECU of a Chicken Oxo cube being unwrapped.

Cut to Nick, at the table again with the family. He looks at the plate in front of him. He turns to his father to complete the double-act.

NICK: I say, I say. Do I dctect a hint of turkey here?

Cut to CU of Dad looking towards Nick.

DAD: Yes, but don't gobble it up all at once.
General disapproval from family.

ECU of Oxo cube being crumbled.

Cut to long shot of family round the table. As Mum enters shot with a dish, the family leaps up and all start making chicken noises and flapping their arms.	Family chicken noises.
Cut to CU of Mum. She does not look very amused.	*MUM*: Oh yes, Ha, Ha. Very amusing. It's kebabs tomorrow.
ECU of meat kebab lying on a bed of rice. A sauce is being poured over the kebab.	
Cut to Alison, at the table, looking at her plate of food while her mother pours sauce over her kebab. She looks up to Mum.	*ALISON*: These kebabs. They're not turkey, are they?
Cut to Mum, standing at the table still holding the sauce boat. She looks round the table and then back to Alison.	*MUM*: Turkish.

- Identify examples of humour in *Turkish*. Do you think the humour works?
- What do ECU and CU stand for? Why has the copywriter used them so frequently?
- What atmosphere is created in the commercial? How would this help 'sell' the product?
- Who is the commercial aimed at?
- The Oxo family has been referred to as a 'soap opera'. Discuss why this might be appropriate.
- What are your favourite TV commercials? Hold a survey in the class or school to see which are the a) favourite b) least favourite commercials. Is there any difference between what adults (teachers, parents) like and what young people enjoy? Do girls and boys differ in their likes/dislikes?
- Are there any commercials currently on television which use

humour to sell the product? Can you think of any other possible types of TV commercial other than humorous?

- Have a go and write a script for one of the following products or companies:

  a luxury toilet soap;
  a hand cleansing cream which will remove paint and oil;
  a motor car;
  a chocolate bar;
  a double glazing firm;
  a chain of grocery stores;
  an electronic game for young children.

Make full use of the 'Vision' and 'Sound' layout. The advertising firm of J. Walter Thompson has created a real sense of atmosphere in its advertising campaign for Oxo. Try and create a suitable atmosphere in your own scripts. Remember to keep your script as economical as possible. Every image you present on screen and every word your characters say should be well thought out. Time is money in advertising.

- If possible make a video of your commercial. You will be amazed at just how much effort and thought goes into those thirty seconds of screen time.

- Research the subject of advertising. Bring into school magazines and newspapers. Video TV commercials and tape radio advertising. Does advertising differ according to the particular outlet? (For example, is there any difference between 'popular' and 'serious' newspapers?) How honest do you think advertisers are? Have you ever been persuaded to buy something purely on the basis of the advertising campaign? Are there any less obvious types of advertising?

- Here is a second script for OXO. After reading it, imagine you are in a meeting to choose the next advert in your television campaign. There are two groups of people. Half of you are representatives for Brooke Bond OXO, the company who commissioned the advertising firm, and the remainder work for J. Walter Thompson, the advertising agency itself. You have to decide which is the most effective advert, *Turkish* or *Wish I Was Dead*. Ignore the fact that one is for Chicken OXO and the other for normal OXO.

In groups of five or six decide who represents which company and act out the meeting

Remember to keep in role. For instance, one of you will have to explain to JWT (your clients) the intentions behind each advert. In order to prepare for this it might be necessary to have a short meeting with your colleagues before the main meeting to plan your strategy and to anticipate possible questions. Likewise, if you are representing OXO, you would probably read the scripts first and draw up a list of possible queries and opinions.

One person in the group should keep minutes of this meeting.

When you have reached your decision one person in the group should report back to the rest of the class. Again, keep in role.

Client BROOKE BOND OXO
Title 'WISH I WAS DEAD'
Length 30 SECONDS

Product RED OXO
Medium TV

VISION	SOUND
	½ second silence.
Open on Mum making the finishing touches to the kitchen table which is obviously set for a special dinner. Dad comes in through the back door carrying a bottle of wine.	*DAD*: Not here yet, then?
Mum turns towards the cooker.	*MUM*: No. Only half an hour late.
Cut to CU of Dad unwrapping the tissue round the bottle.	*DAD*: I don't know why we're going to all this trouble.
Cut to ECU of Oxo cube being crumbled.	
Cut to CU of Mum turning towards Dad.	*MUM*: He's your brother!
Cut to CU of Dad turning back towards Mum.	*DAD*: Yes. And you invited them!
Cut to Mum bringing the roasting tin out of the oven. Dad comes in to help as Mum puts the tin down	*DAD*: A glass of beer and a pie would have been enough! *MUM*: Alright, alright! Just

on the work surface.

give me a hand will you.

Cut to the table as Alison enters. She looks at the elaborate table setting.,

(Mum and Dad mumbling in the background)
ALISON: Who's all this for?

Cut back to Mum lifting a joint of pork from the tin that Dad is holding.

MUM: Uncle Bob and Auntie Jean, of course.

Cut to ECU of the pork being placed on a platter surrounded by stuffing balls and cherry tomatoes in apple rings.

Cut to MS of Alison. She begins to look worried.

ALISON: But they rang this morning to say they couldn't...come.

Cut to back view of Mum and Dad still busy at the work surface. They stop suddenly and turn towards Alison in unison, Mum still holding the meat fork. Dad restrains Mum.

MUM: Alison!
DAD: No.

Cut back to Alison looking guilty.

Writing from Experience: Extended Study

Several readers have commented that Helen Cresswell's play evokes very warm memories of their childhood Christmases. Creating an atmosphere in your writing is vital. In one of my short stories I tried to describe a village pub from my childhood in Cumbria. I was only seven or so at the time but this was what I remember it looked like on the morning I first arrived:

> *'Every room was an adventure. From my bedroom window at the back I could see the blue waters of the Solway Firth. The bar smelt of beer and tobacco. The cellar was dark and mysterious with huge, swollen barrels of beer. The bottles on the shelves were stamped with colourful labels and lovely names like Nut Brown and Milk Stout. There was a dart board, a snooker table, bar skittles, pictures*

and trophies. I was mad with excitement and tore from room to room yelling out at each discovery.'

The story from which this is taken, 'The Scythe,' (*Dreams and Resolutions,* ed. Roy Blatchford, Unwin Hyman) was largely fictional, but this particular memory of my childhood home is as accurate as I can make it. As a teacher myself I know that often the best writing handed in to me by my pupils is that based on their real experience.

The following tasks are intended to improve your writing by asking you to remember your childhood. It starts initially with the activity that was in the Follow On section for *Jackie's First Day.*

A Memory Game

1 Describe your first morning at your present school.
2 Describe your last day at your previous school. What stands out? What did your classroom look like? Describe your teacher. Can you remember any incidents that took place during that school year?
3 Go back in time, class by class, to your very first teacher and class. Once again, try and recollect memories from that year. Share these memories with the rest of the class.
4 What is the earliest memory you have? Be careful here—at this point people often 'remember' things they have been told about by relations, not what they can actually remember themselves.
5 If you enjoyed the activities try telling a partner some of your other memories of a) childhood b) previous homes c) holidays.

- If you had to choose the strongest memory (for whatever reason) from your childhood, what would it be? Tell your partner and then see if there is anything you and the rest of the class have in common. If possible tape these conversations and make a transcript of them. You should have the basis of some first class writing although there will need to be some work in shaping and polishing your final draft.

- Use the heading 'An Extract From My Autobiography'. You should aim to describe what happened in such clear detail that your reader will be able to really picture the experience. Share your writing with the rest of the class.

- If you would prefer, write a script covering a chosen moment from your past. As you write, read it out to yourself to ensure you manage to capture the real flavour of the dialogue.

Other People's Experiences

- Go to the library and examine the fiction section carefully. Scanning the books, see if you can discover writing that seems to have been based on first hand experience. Note features in the writing that you can use yourself. Read out your chosen extract to the rest of the class. Explain your reasons for choosing that particular passage.

I Remember, I Remember

- An effective poem can be created by the class as a whole in the following way.

Each member of the class has one line only of a poem to write. These lines will fit into verses of four lines, each of which begins with the words, *I remember, I remember...* You must choose one experience from your childhood and attempt to compress everything into one line of poetry. When you have done this, group the lines into fours—perhaps with a common theme, and then read it out in class with each person reading out the line they wrote.

- Each member of the class can write a whole *verse*, or you can write your own entire poem. The key point with poetry is that you have to select your words carefully. It forces you to think about language.

Other People's Memories

- Of course it is not only you who have memories of your childhood. Your parents/friends/relatives/neighbours will also have memories of some of the things you did when you were younger. It is interesting to compare notes. Different people remember different things. Using a notebook to record what they say (or preferably a tape recorder) talk with them about your childhood. Write up your conversations and place their accounts side by side with yours, to contrast what people remember best.

- An interesting variation is to choose a particular place—a market, park, school, factory, etc.—and see if you can get different generations of people to talk about their memories of the place.

Your Photograph Album

- Most families have lots of photographs. Simply describing in words a picture you have in front of you can lead to powerful, atmospheric writing. Choose a picture from your family album and bring it to school. Write about what is taking place, then display your work together with the picture in the classroom.

Your Own Future Writing

- Next time you write a poem, story, or drama script set it firmly in a real place. You should find your writing is improved beyond recognition. Remember, the whole story may not be true, but basing your writing on what *is* true will make everything more fresh and readable.

Writing for Real Audiences: Extended Study

In his personal essay, Phil Lowe writes, 'most of the plays I have written have been effectively written to order' and adds that professional writers live by 'turning their hand to whatever needs doing.' Quite independently, Rony Robinson relates how he had to write the script for *Naughty Girls* because 'on Wednesday morning a dozen schoolteachers would be meeting at the local radio station to record the play I hadn't written yet.'

Your work in English will improve if you are actually writing for a real purpose. This section gives you a choice of some real tasks for writing and talking. However, for starters perhaps the best tip you can have is to set yourself a deadline. I know from bitter experience that if I set my class a piece of homework and tell them I want it in for, say, 'a week or so', I don't get it in for several weeks or so. If I say 'Deadline Tuesday, period 4' there's a chance most assignments will be completed by that date. If my pupils say, 'I've done it, Sir, it's just that I've left it at home, my grandma's, my friend's, blah blah blah', there's a good chance they will work all night to get it in the next morning. They've set themselves the deadline.

Writing for Your School

● There are people in all schools who are responsible for writing. I know from experience that they will gladly welcome help from an enthusiastic class. Here are three of the main writing tasks my own school undertakes each year:

A handbook for new pupils

A third year options booklet

A newsletter to parents

In some schools, pupils themselves contribute to the production of these publications. Why not ask your teachers if this might be possible for you? By sharing the various tasks among the class it should be possible to cover each aspect in greater detail than one teacher would have time for.

● There are handbooks for the first/third/fifth year but I have never seen one for the second or fourth year. This seems a shame. Why not produce one?

Assemblies

● All schools have assemblies. Preparing the work week in, week out, can be a major problem for those teachers involved. Again, I know from experience that they would jump at the chance if a class offered to take over an assembly. If you have worked on a play and need an audience, why not see the teachers concerned. It may well be that there are themes or subjects that need to be covered in the year's assemblies. Why not see what they are and prepare your script accordingly?

Competitions

● Competitions are marvellous ways of attracting interest. In the course of a year schools receive information about lots of different ones, both local and national. As a change from entering someone else's competition, why not organise your own within the school? Decide just what you want to be judged. Is it to be a competition for poetry, short stories, plays, descriptive writing, drama? What are to be your rules? Is it to be for all age groups? How are you going to advertise the competition? Is it to be just for your school? What are to be your prizes? Can you obtain sponsorship from local firms or organisations? Who is to judge? Are you going to arrange press coverage? Where are the entries to be displayed? Where is the presentation to take place?

Until you actually organise something like this you can have no idea of the work involved. But look at the talking and writing involved in the above. For instance, obtaining sponsorship will involve writing many letters, and they must be impressive: a firm is unlikely to look kindly on a scruffy, badly produced letter or respond positively to a visitor who seems only to have dreamt up the matter on the way from school.

Local Newspapers

● Newspapers have very limited resources to cover all the news stories in their area. It may well be that there is some issue that is crying out for coverage in the local paper. Contact the editor and ask if you can write an article on a particular subject. It will need to be well researched. Issues I have seen raised in this way have included the environment, law and order, unemployment, leisure facilities, and education. Some newspapers have a policy of encouraging youngsters to write or take part.

Local Radio

● The same is true for radio. Short stories, magazine-type programmes, playscripts, public speaking, interviews, poems etc. will all receive sympathetic attention if the station manager is approached in a sensible manner. If you can record it yourselves so much the better.

Community Drama

● A growing and welcome trend is for drama groups to produce their own plays about the local community or the environment. There are obvious opportunities for aspiring playwrights. If you look at your local newpaper or contact your local theatre you will find people to approach.

Infant Junior Schools

● Children love listening to stories. If you want to test your skills as a story teller, either with your own material or someone else's, ask your teachers if they can contact nearby schools and arrange a visit. Or if you have a short play to perform, a class of infants can be a marvellous audience.

Final Note

● Writing for yourself, the teacher and the exercise book can be a desperately lonely business. Share your work.

Acting and Memorising: Extended Study

This section assumes that you are going to produce one of the plays.

Firstly, choose one of the plays to work on. Discount the ages of the characters as far as possible. All of you will be older than the young children in Helen Cresswell's play, yet it could easily be acted out by teenagers. (A very famous and successful Dennis Potter play was once produced for television with adults playing all the children's roles.) Again, some of the roles are for adults. You will have to act these yourself.

● *Casting*

Working in groups, choose a member of the class to act out each of the characters in the script. It is not always a good idea to match people to particular characters purely because they are similar in character. It might, for example, take a very self-confident person to act out the part of a shy person.

Write down your provisional cast list and compare it with those of other groups.

How do the members of the class feel about acting out the characters?

Decide on your final list.

● *Learning the lines*

How do you set about remembering lines? In some plays actors and actresses have a huge amount to remember. How do they do it?

This is how *not* to do it: decide on a common starting point for each member of the class, preferably where one character does all or most of the speaking.

You have five minutes to remember as much of the script as possible. You must work alone. You must not speak out aloud, and you must not write anything down...

How did you do? I'll hazard a guess—not very well!

Discuss amongst yourselves the problems you faced in remembering your lines. Was there anyone who was more successful than the rest in remembering the lines? Has this person any tips?

There are several ways of improving your memory and helping you to remember your lines. Try some of these tips and see if they help you.

- Look at the following list of 50 words. You have three minutes to study them. When the time is up shut the book and write down as many as you can remember. This time you may ignore any of the rules you were given in the earlier exercise.

stool trowel submarine island fridge
table fish spade cushion soil
dandelion saucepan fork axe tin-opener
stove freezer anchor yacht curtains
sofa knife turf roses windows
rake carpet pictures mower rockery
life-jacket sink teapot ocean docks
piano peeler drainer plant larder
swimmer fire bikini worm shelf
liner telephone crocus television armchair

How did you do? Discuss your progress, (or lack of it,) with the class.

- Very often people panic when faced by a list like this, or by a large number of lines in a play. You must always think about what is being asked of you. If you look at the list of words you will notice that it is possible to break it down into groups of words that have something in common. For instance some of the words are to do with the sea. What other groups are there in the above list?

- Lines in a play will not fall into groups but they do have a context. A character will speak in a certain way because of a particular situation. If you panic and simply try and remember a group of random words you will fail. If you can actually imagine the situation and the character of the person you are playing, you will have a far greater chance of remembering your lines. Even reading out your lines with expression will help.

- Another tip is to break down your lines into small, manageable sections. Some of you will have done this with your list of words. Learn a small section, test yourself (or get someone to test you), check your lines, repeat and add a few more lines, repeat, and so on...

- Acting out a scene can be fun especially if you work in small groups and help each other. Ensure you have enough space to work in. You should ideally be able to work without distraction. Ask your teacher if the hall or other large area is available.

- After reading out the script, try acting out a small section of it. You needn't try to get every line perfectly accurate. Build up to this. If the play is well written the lines will seem perfectly natural when they are read out.

- Read again what Jan Mark has written in her personal essay about setting her play against some background action—in the case of *Feet* this was a tennis match. Decide what your character can be doing as you deliver your lines. One of the easiest ways of distinguishing the professional from the amateur actor or actress is to watch them closely; professionals always seem to have plenty of time to deliver their lines—they will quite naturally pause to remove a bit of fluff from their jacket or to stretch or comb their hair; anything; in fact, that gives the appearance of reality.

- Finally if you are to produce one of the plays for an audience there are many activities involved in addition to acting. Look at the list of credits at the end of any film and you will realise just what is involved. Some of the following might be more in your line:

designing the programme;
choosing or producing the background music;
costume design;
scenery design and construction;
selecting the location (for a film);
producing the sound effects, special effects, lighting;
publicity;
directing the play.

- All these scripts were written for production. There is arguably nothing so exciting during your time in school as assisting in the production of a school play.

Writing a Speech: Extended Study

This is the text for a speech fifteen year Victoria Greathead made in a recent Public Speaking Competition organised by The British Junior Chamber of Commerce.

When you speak in public, you have to be thoroughly prepared. Due to the pressures of the situation, it is almost impossible to make your speech up as you go along. All experienced speakers prepare their talks or speeches in advance. The trick is to make everything *appear* as natural as possible.

Victoria's speech is carefully designed to persuade. What is most impressive is her ability to deal with a serious and controversial subject in a lively and humorous manner. Her title was hardly an easy one: *'Genetic Engineering: When Should Man Stop Playing God?'*

As you read it, notice the following points:

— how she asks questions to involve her audience;
— the way in which she uses humour;
— her choice of language and, especially, any particularly clever sequences of words;
— her careful presentation of scientific information and her choice of examples.

Mr Chairman, ladies and gentlemen,

So you don't believe in genetic engineering, do you? Sound a little too much like Frankenstein, does it? Man creates a monster that eventually destroys him. Scientists meddle with embryos: anyone second rate, short sighted, short legged, short on energy, short on sense, is eliminated.

All this, ladies and gentlemen, is the subject of nightmares —wonderful territory for Hammer Films or Steven Spielberg to exploit, but it's about as accurate and realistic as E.T. or Christopher Lee's teeth.

Saying we should give up genetic engineering is like saying we shouldn't fly because we have no wings, or that the Earth is flat because we can't see over the horizon.

When I came to this subject I was full of such prejudices. But we've been tampering with nature for almost as long as Eve discovered Adam. How many of you enjoyed a glass of wine this Christmas? Your wine probably came from grapes fermented in the vat, the bacteria transforming the sugar into alcohol. The vines from which the grapes came were the product of selective breeding; nothing is naturally so prolific.

For breakfast, maybe you had Shredded Wheat: 'Nothing added, nothing taken away.' But that's not true. We don't chew wild grass anymore. The grasses have been selected, the grains are swollen, the stems short; ideal for quantity and ease of harvesting. Selected and crossbred to give that 'natural' fibre-rich start to the day! This blouse comes from cotton plants specially bred to produce ever more of the fluffy white stuff. The cows in our fields are not the same breed we would have seen one hundred, fifty, even twenty years ago. The fields, countryside, environment are not the same.

Man has played God throughout his history; selective breeding has gone on ever since woman first dragged man into her cave!

Of course, selective breeding is not strictly speaking, genetic engineering. Engineering implies something more exact, like oil that can slide down and fit perfectly into a spanner.

When I asked my Biology teacher what genetic engineering was, he said: 'Ah, recombinant D.N.A. technology, Victoria.'

'D.N.A.?' I replied.

'Deoxyribose nucleic acid.'

'Recombinant?' said I.

'Monoclonal antibodies,' said he.

Panicking, I asked for a more simple explanation.

'When scientists attach genetic material into bacteria which are capable of putting it back into another organism.'

Genetic engineering is so new it's frightening, although it is reassuring to learn that Britain leads the way in this state of the arts, biological revolution.

Insulin can now be produced by this process. Usually it's done by killing animals. Diabetics use animal insulin, which can have side effects: blindness and kidney failure. But now, by the activities of bacteria through genetic engineering, we can obtain human insulin that is pure and free from side effects.

You see, genetic engineering is basically getting bacteria to do our work. Placed in huge fermenting vats bacteria duplicate themselves every twenty minutes. Doesn't sound spectacular? If you put one grain of rice on the first square of a chess board, two on the second and kept doubling, by the time you got to the 64th square there wouldn't be enough grains of rice in the world to fit on it. So we're dealing in pretty big numbers!

No wonder scientists are getting excited. Bacteria are wonderful. You've heard of the mighty micro, well we're in the age of the beautiful bacteria.

In Brazil 90 per cent of cars run on alcohol—I think they call it Gasohol—bacteria has turned sugary plants into alcohol. No lead, no devouring the Earth's finite resources and no pollution. Genetic engineering at its best.

Why kill animals when bacteria can create protein? It's true, vegetarians rejoice, there is hope. Thanks to the beautiful bacteria.

In the world of medicine, genetic engineering offers hope against inherited disorders: Downs syndrome, haemophilia, cystic fibrosis. Are we saying we should just crawl back into the Dark Ages and ignore these?

God gave us free will, Mr Chairman. Genetic engineering will assist mankind. Anything, in the wrong hands, is potentially evil. A scalpel can harm as well heal, but we don't stop using it because of this, do we?

(*Text of a speech delivered to the Doncaster Junior Chamber of Commerce in the National Schools' Public Speaking Contest, January 1987. Victoria won the Junior Competition.*)

- You may not agree with Victoria's argument. It would be quite possible to argue equally convincingly that genetic engineering is wrong. In that case you would have to select examples to prove your point. You would have to slant your speech differently. You would, however, need to use some of the debating tricks Victoria uses in her speech. Discuss Victoria Greathead's speech using the four points referred to earlier. Two definitions might prove useful:

  rhetoric: 'the art of persuasive or impressive writing; language designed to persuade or impress.' (*The Concise Oxford Dictionary*)

  rhetorical question: 'A question is often put not to elicit information, but as a more striking substitute for a statement. The assumption is that only one answer is possible, and that if the hearer is compelled to make it mentally himself it will impress him more than the speaker's statement.' (*Fowler's Modern English Usage*)

- Make a list of the people (and occasions) most likely to use rhetoric. A politician is a prime example, but can you think of any less obvious cases?

- Have a class debate in which two opposing teams must argue their point and attempt to persuade the majority. This is how to do it.

1 Decide on a formal proposal (the motion) on which you will have to vote.
2 One team proposes the motion, the other opposes it.
3 Choose an issue where there is likely to be strong feelings either way.
4 Decide how many speakers will be in each team. Elect one member as the main speaker.
5 Give the speakers plenty of time to prepare their speeches.
6 Set time limits, say five minutes for the main speaker on each side, three minutes for the supporting speakers.
7 Choose someone to chair the debate.

8 Allow questions 'from the floor' after the speakers have finished.
9 Allow one person from each team to sum up.
10 Take a vote at the end of the speeches.
11 Publish your final result, (whether the motion was carried or defeated).

About The Writers

Phil Lowe wanted to be a writer from an early age—he wrote his first novel (a science fiction blockbuster) at the age of eight, but had to wait another nine years to see his first published work, a short story for teenagers called *Six Months*. At this stage he developed a parallel interest in acting, and after studying English at Cambridge University, he trained as an actor at the Drama Studio, London, which led to a two-year stint as a writer and performer with Touchstone Theatre-in-Education in Essex. He has written several plays for schools, many covering topical themes such as drug and alcohol abuse, and an adaptation of Charles Dickens' *Great Expectations* for the Rank Educational Trust. He has also written comedy scripts for the BBC Radio and Capital Radio in London. Aside from his own written work, he runs writing workshops for the Eastern Arts Association.

Jan Mark is one of today's most successful writers for young people. Her work has not only sold well but has been distgringuished by a series of literary awards. She has, for example, achieved the rare feat of twice being awarded the prestigious Library Association's Carnegie Medal for *Thunder and Lightnings* in 1976 and *Handles* in 1983. Her collection of stories, from which the script *Feet* is derived, *Feet and Other Stories*, itself won the Angel Literary Prize. Other books that are 'musts' include *Under the Autumn Sky, Nothing to be Afraid Of, Hairs in the Palm of Her Hand*, and *The Ennead*. Sensitive, witty and always highly original, all her work can be highly recommended.

She is married with two children and lives in Oxford.

Ian Lumsden was born in Carlisle, Cumbria. He has taught in secondary schools in Liverpool and Doncaster. Until recently he was Head of English and Drama. *Scriptz* is his first book—the first of many, he hopes. He is married with two lovely daughters.

Rony Robinson Almost a hundred of his plays have been performed since 1971, in theatres all over England, and on the radio and TV. He has been Arts Council resident playwright at the Theatre Royal Stratford East and at Deptford Green School in London. He has published four historical novels for 'young adults' of which *A Time of Bears* is the best, and *Rebecca's Story*, giving Judas's sister's version of the Crucifixion, is best known. His peculiar play about a kid whose family split up, *Frankly Frankie*, is widely used in schools and unexpectedly for GCSE. His best work, he says, is *The Beano*. Broadcast by Radio 4, staged at Derby, Leeds and elsewhere, it's all about a day trip to Scarborough by a Yorkshire brewery in 1914. It is also published as a novel. He is currently finishing a children's novel about a dad who becomes a Punch and Judy man and a kid who doesn't believe him.

Rony Robinson has three children who tell better tales than he does, and is morning disc jockey on BBC Radio Sheffield.

Helen Cresswell is well known for her books for children. The hugely comic *The Bagthorpe Saga* is a firm favourite with everyone. Her magical and beautifully written fantasies (*The Piemakers, The Night-Watchmen, Where the Wind Blows, The Bongleweed* and *The Secret World of Polly Flint*—to mention only a few of her forty or so books) are all stamped with the syle and narrative flair that is her hallmark. Her novel for teenagers, *Dear Shrink*, is another not to miss.

She is married with two children and lives in Nottinghamshire.

Further Reading

The books in this entirely arbitrary selection of texts are not necessarily funny books. Indeed, Raymond Briggs' *When the Wind Blows*, is not in any way funny. As it has, however, used the comic strip format, and as it is an incredibly moving book, I have no reservations about its inclusion. What I have attempted to do is to offer a varied selection of texts which fall within a very broad definition of the word 'humour'. I have made no attempt to differentiate between novels, short stories, poetry, or drama scripts—they're all good and worth reading.

Ahlberg, Allan: *Please Mrs Butler*, Puffin;
Blatchford, Roy (ed.): *A Roald Dahl Selection*, Longman;
Blatchford, Roy (ed.): *Openings*, Unwin Hyman;
Bowles, Steve (ed.): *Mischief Makers*, Collins;
Brace, Geoffrey: *All Aboard*, Macmillan;
Briggs, Raymond: *When The Wind Blows*, Hamish Hamilton;
Browne, Anthony & MacRae, Julia: *Gorrilla*, Magnet;
Brownjohn, Sandy & Whitaker, Janet: *Wordgames*, Hodder & Stoughton;
Byars, Betsy: *The - Not - Just - Anybody Family*, Collins;
Dahl, Roald: *Revolting Rhymes*, Puffin;
Dahl, Roald: *Boy*, Heinemann;
Dahl, Roald: *Going Solo*, Heinemann;
Fraine, Laurie (ed.): *I Told You So: Stories of Family Life*, Collins;
Forsyth, Bill: *Gregory's Girl* (the play, adapted by Andrew Bethell) Cambridge University Press;
Davies, Lesley: *Superhero*, Longman;
Fine, Anne: *A Pack of Lies*, Hamish Hamilton;
Fine, Anne: *Madame Doubtfire*, Hamish Hamilton;
Finney, Eric: *Billy and Me at the Church Hall Sale and Other Poems*, Hodder & Stoughton;
Gilmore, Kate: *Of Griffins and Graffiti*, Puffin Plus;
Gower, Mick: *Swings and Roundabouts*, Collins;
Harmer, David, Macmillan, Ian & Wiley, Martyn: *Overstone*, Arnold Wheaton;
Heide, Florence Parry: *The Shrinking of Treehorn* Viking Kestrel;
Holman, David: *Football Apprentices*, Cambridge University Press;
Horton, Peter: *Ossie and Thwartz*, Macmillan;
Ireson, Barbara: *In a Class of Their Own*, Heinemann;
Lingard, Joan: *Rags and Riches*, Hamish Hamilton;
Lee, Anne: *Faust and Furious*, Cambridge University Press;
McGough,Roger: *Strictly Private*, Puffin;
Martin, William: *Vacuees*, Cambridge University Press;
Naughton, Bill: *Late Night on Watling Street and Other Stories*, Longman;
Oakley, Graham: *Henry's Quest*, Macmillan;
Oldham, June: *Enter Tom*, Viking Kestrel;

Parker, Alan: *Bugsey Malone:The Play*, Collins:
Patten, Brian: *Gargling with Jelly*, Puffin:
Phinn, Gervase: *Perci*, Longman;
Phinn, Gervase: *Right on Cue*, Unwin Hyman;
Phinn, Gervase: *Stage Write*, Unwin Hyman;
Pilling, Ann: *Henry's Leg*, Puffin;
Ridgeway, Bill: *Comedy Scripts:The Two Ronnies*, Macmillan;
Rosenthal, Jack: *P'tang, Yang, Kipperbang and Other TV Plays*, (edited by Alison Leake), Longman;
Sadler/Hayllmar/Powell, (eds.): *Plays of Humour and Suspense*, Macmillan;
Scott, Rachel: *A Wedding Man is Nicer than Cats Miss'*, Heinemann;
Townsend, Sue: *The Secret Diary of Adrian Mile, Aged 13½*, Macmillan;
Styles, Morag: *I Like That Stuff*, Cambridge University Press;
Ure, Jean: *A Proper Little Nooryeff*, Bodley Head;
Wersba, Barbara: *Tones For A Small Harmonica*, Bodley Head.

Unwin Hyman English Series

Series editor: Roy Blatchford
Advisers: Jane Leggett and Gervase Phinn

Unwin Hyman Short Stories

Openings edited by Roy Blatchford
Round Two edited by Roy Blatchford
School's OK edited by Josie Karavasil and Roy Blatchford
Stepping Out edited by Jane Leggett
That'll Be The Day edited by Roy Blatchford
Sweet and Sour edited by Gervase Phinn
It's Now or Never edited by Jane Leggett and Roy Blatchford
Pigs is Pigs edited by Trevor Millum
Dreams and Resolutions edited by Roy Blatchford
Snakes and Ladders edited by H.T. Robertson
Shorties edited by Roy Blatchford
First Class edited by Michael Bennett
Crime Busters edited by Barry Pateman and Jennie Sidney

Unwin Hyman Collections

Free As I Know edited by Beverley Naidoo
Solid Ground edited by Jane Leggett and Sue Libovitch
In Our Image edited by Andrew Goodwyn
Funnybones edited by Trevor Millum
Northern Lights edited by Leslie Wheeler and Douglas Young

Unwin Hyman Plays

Stage Write edited by Gervase Phinn
Right on Cue edited by Gervase Phinn

ACKNOWLEDGEMENTS

The editor and publisher are very grateful to the following for permission to reproduce the plays and extracts which appear in this book:

Helen Cresswell for 'For Bethlehem, Read Little Thraves', reproduced by permission of A M Heath & Co.

Phil Lowe for 'Jackie's First Day'.

Jan Mark for 'Feet', reproduced by permission of Murray Pollinger.

Rony Robinson for 'Naughty Girls' and 'How Mavis Met Gary Blood'.

J Walter Thomson for the two *Oxo* advert scripts.